BASIC NUMERACY
AND STATISTICS

Pearson

At Pearson, we have a simple mission: to help people make more of their lives through learning.

We combine innovative learning technology with trusted content and educational expertise to provide engaging and effective learning experience that serve people wherever and whenever they are learning.

We enable our customers to access a wide and expanding range of market-leading content from world-renowned authors and develop their own tailor-made book. From classroom to boardroom, our curriculum materials, digital learning tools and testing programmes help to educate millions of people worldwide — more than any other private enterprise.

Every day our work helps learning flourish, and wherever learning flourishes, so do people.

To learn more, please visit us at: www.pearson.com/uk

THIRD EDITION

BASIC NUMERACY AND STATISTICS

Selected chapters from:

Foundation Maths
Seventh edition
Anthony Croft & Robert Davison

Basic Business Statistics Concepts and Applications
Fourteenth edition | Global edition
Mark L. Berenson, David M. Levine, Kathryn A. Szabat & David F. Stephan

 Pearson

Harlow, England • London • New York • Boston • San Francisco • Toronto • Sydney • Dubai • Singapore • Hong Kong
Tokyo • Seoul • Taipei • New Dehli • Cape Town • São Paulo • Mexico City • Madrid • Amsterdam • Munich • Paris • Milan

Pearson
KAO Two
KAO Park
Harlow
Essex CM17 9NA

And associated companies throughout the world

Visit us on the World Wide Web at:
www.pearson.com/uk

© Pearson Education Limited 2020

Compiled from:

Foundation Maths
Seventh edition
Anthony Croft & Robert Davison
ISBN 978-1-292-28968-7
© Pearson Education Limited 1995, 2003, 2006, 2010 (print)
© Pearson Education Limited 2016, 2020 (print and electronic)

Basic Business Statistics Concepts and Applications
Fourteenth edition | Global edition
Mark L. Berenson, David M. Levine, Kathryn A. Szabat & David F. Stephan
ISBN 978-1-292-26503-2
© Pearson Education Limited 2020

ISBN 978-1-83961-788-1

Printed and bound in Great Britain by CPI Group.

CONTENTS

Arithmetic of whole numbers

1

Objectives: This chapter:

- explains the rules for adding, subtracting, multiplying and dividing positive and negative numbers
- explains what is meant by an integer
- explains what is meant by a prime number
- explains what is meant by a factor
- explains how to prime factorise an integer
- explains the terms 'highest common factor' and 'lowest common multiple'

1.1 Addition, subtraction, multiplication and division

Arithmetic is the study of numbers and their manipulation. A clear and firm understanding of the rules of arithmetic is essential for tackling everyday calculations. Arithmetic also serves as a springboard for tackling more abstract mathematics such as algebra and calculus.

The calculations in this chapter will involve mainly whole numbers, or **integers** as they are often called. The **positive integers** are the numbers

$$1, 2, 3, 4, 5 \ldots$$

and the **negative integers** are the numbers

$$\ldots -5, -4, -3, -2, -1$$

The dots (. . .) indicate that this sequence of numbers continues indefinitely. The number 0 is also an integer but is neither positive nor negative.

To find the **sum** of two or more numbers, the numbers are added together. To find the **difference** of two numbers, the second is subtracted from the first. The **product** of two numbers is found by multiplying the numbers together. Finally, the **quotient** of two numbers is found by dividing the first number by the second.

WORKED EXAMPLE

1.1   (a)   Find the sum of 3, 6 and 4.

(b)   Find the difference of 6 and 4.

(c)   Find the product of 7 and 2.

(d)   Find the quotient of 20 and 4.

Solution   (a)   The sum of 3, 6 and 4 is

$$3 + 6 + 4 = 13$$

(b)   The difference of 6 and 4 is

$$6 - 4 = 2$$

(c)   The product of 7 and 2 is

$$7 \times 2 = 14$$

(d)   The quotient of 20 and 4 is $\frac{20}{4}$, that is 5.

When writing products we sometimes replace the sign $\times$ by '·' or even omit it completely. For example, $3 \times 6 \times 9$ could be written as $3 \cdot 6 \cdot 9$ or $(3)(6)(9)$.

On occasions it is necessary to perform calculations involving negative numbers. To understand how these are added and subtracted consider Figure 1.1, which shows a **number line.**

Figure 1.1
The number line

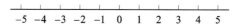

Any number can be represented by a point on the line. Positive numbers are on the right-hand side of the line and negative numbers are on the left. From any given point on the line, we can add a positive number by moving that number of places to the right. For example, to find the sum $5 + 3$, start at the point 5 and move 3 places to the right, to arrive at 8. This is shown in Figure 1.2.

Figure 1.2
To add a positive number, move that number of places to the right

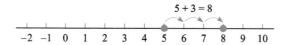

To subtract a positive number, we move that number of places to the left. For example, to find the difference $5 - 7$, start at the point 5 and move 7 places to the left to arrive at -2. Thus $5 - 7 = -2$. This is shown in Figure 1.3. The result of finding $-3 - 4$ is also shown to be -7.

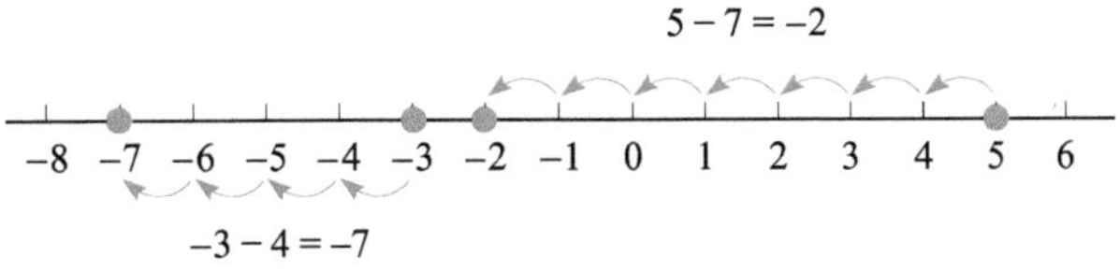

Figure 1.3
To subtract a positive number, move that number of places to the left

$$5 - 7 = -2$$

$$-3 - 4 = -7$$

To add a negative number we move to the left. The result of finding $2 + (-3)$ is shown in Figure 1.4. Starting at 2, we move 3 places to the left, to arrive at -1.

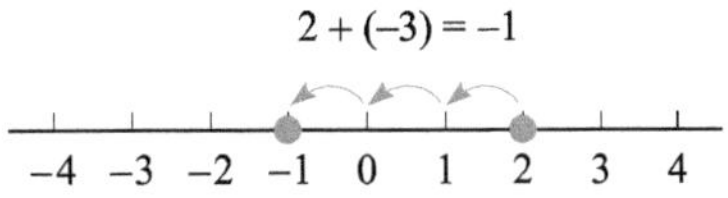

Figure 1.4
Adding a negative number involves moving to the left

$$2 + (-3) = -1$$

We see that $2 + (-3) = -1$. Note that this is the same as the result of finding $2 - 3$, so that adding a negative number is equivalent to subtracting a positive number. For example

$$9+(-4) = 9-4 = 5, 3+(-7) = 3-7 = -4, -6+(-10) = -6-10 = -16$$

To subtract a negative number we move to the right. The result of finding $5 - (-3)$ is shown in Figure 1.5

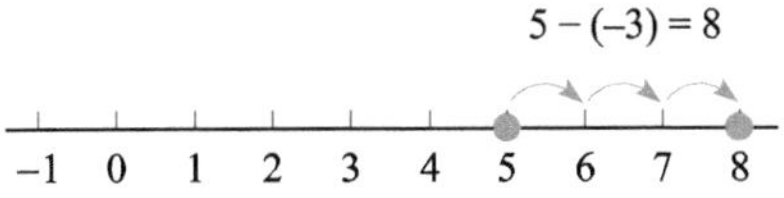

Figure 1.5
Subtracting a negative number involves moving to the right

$$5 - (-3) = 8$$

We see that $5 - (-3) = 8$. This is the same as the result of finding $5+3$, so subtracting a negative number is equivalent to adding a positive number. For example

$$6-(-2) = 6+2 = 8, -5-(-3) = -5 + 3 = -2, -1-(-1) = -1+1 = 0$$

Key point

Adding a negative number is equivalent to subtracting a positive number.
Subtracting a negative number is equivalent to adding a positive number.

WORKED EXAMPLE

1.2 Evaluate (a) $8 + (-4)$, (b) $-15 + (-3)$, (c) $-15 - (-4)$.

Solution (a) $8 + (-4)$ is equivalent to $8 - 4$, that is 4.

(b) Because adding a negative number is equivalent to subtracting a positive number we find $-15 + (-3)$ is equivalent to $-15 - 3$, that is -18.

(c) $-15 - (-4)$ is equivalent to $-15 + 4$, that is -11.

When we need to multiply or divide negative numbers, care must be taken with the **sign** of the answer; that is, whether the result is positive or negative. The following rules apply for determining the sign of the answer when multiplying or dividing positive and negative numbers.

Key point

(positive) $\times$ (positive) $=$ positive   and $\dfrac{\text{positive}}{\text{positive}} = \text{positive}$

(positive) $\times$ (negative) $=$ negative

(negative) $\times$ (positive) $=$ negative

(negative) $\times$ (negative) $=$ positive $\dfrac{\text{positive}}{\text{negative}} = \text{negative}$

$\dfrac{\text{negative}}{\text{positive}} = \text{negative}$

$\dfrac{\text{negative}}{\text{negative}} = \text{positive}$

WORKED EXAMPLE

1.3   Evaluate

(a) $3 \times (-2)$ (b) $(-1) \times 7$ (c) $(-2) \times (-4)$ (d) $\dfrac{12}{(-4)}$ (e) $\dfrac{-8}{4}$ (f) $\dfrac{-6}{-2}$

Solution

(a) We have a positive number, 3, multiplied by a negative number, -2, and so the result will be negative:

$$3 \times (-2) = -6$$

(b) $(-1) \times 7 = -7$

(c) Here we have two negative numbers being multiplied and so the result will be positive:

$$(-2) \times (-4) = 8$$

(d) A positive number, 12, divided by a negative number, -4, gives a negative result:

$$\frac{12}{-4} = -3$$

(e) A negative number, -8, divided by a positive number, 4, gives a negative result:

$$\frac{-8}{4} = -2$$

(f) A negative number, -6, divided by a negative number, -2, gives a positive result:

$$\frac{-6}{-2} = 3$$

Self-assessment questions 1.1

1. Explain what is meant by an integer, a positive integer and a negative integer.

2. Explain the terms sum, difference, product and quotient.

3. State the sign of the result obtained after performing the following calculations:
    (a) $(-5) \times (-3)$ (b) $(-4) \times 2$ (c) $\frac{7}{-2}$ (d) $\frac{-8}{-4}$.

Exercise 1.1

1. Without using a calculator, evaluate each of the following:
    (a) $6 + (-3)$ (b) $6 - (-3)$
    (c) $16 + (-5)$ (d) $16 - (-5)$
    (e) $27 - (-3)$ (f) $27 - (-29)$
    (g) $-16 + 3$ (h) $-16 + (-3)$
    (i) $-16 - 3$ (j) $-16 - (-3)$
    (k) $-23 + 52$ (l) $-23 + (-52)$
    (m) $-23 - 52$ (n) $-23 - (-52)$

2. Without using a calculator, evaluate
    (a) $3 \times (-8)$ (b) $(-4) \times 8$ (c) $15 \times (-2)$
    (d) $(-2) \times (-8)$ (e) $14 \times (-3)$

3. Without using a calculator, evaluate
    (a) $\frac{15}{-3}$ (b) $\frac{21}{7}$ (c) $\frac{-21}{7}$ (d) $\frac{-21}{-7}$ (e) $\frac{21}{-7}$
    (f) $\frac{-12}{2}$ (g) $\frac{-12}{-2}$ (h) $\frac{12}{-2}$

4. Find the sum and product of (a) 3 and 6, (b) 10 and 7, (c) 2, 3 and 6.

5. Find the difference and quotient of (a) 18 and 9, (b) 20 and 5, (c) 100 and 20.

1.2 The BODMAS rule

When evaluating numerical expressions we need to know the order in which addition, subtraction, multiplication and division are carried out. As a simple example, consider evaluating $2 + 3 \times 4$. If the addition is carried out first we get $2 + 3 \times 4 = 5 \times 4 = 20$. If the multiplication is carried out first we get $2 + 3 \times 4 = 2 + 12 = 14$. Clearly the order of carrying out numerical operations is important. The BODMAS rule tells us the order in which we must carry out the operations of addition, subtraction, multiplication and division.

Key point

BODMAS stands for

Brackets ( )	First priority
Of $\times$	Second priority
Division $\div$	Second priority
Multiplication $\times$	Second priority
Addition $+$	Third priority
Subtraction $-$	Third priority

This is the order of carrying out arithmetical operations, with bracketed expressions having highest priority and subtraction and addition having the lowest priority. Note that 'Of', 'Division' and 'Multiplication' have equal priority, as do 'Addition' and 'Subtraction'. 'Of' is used to show multiplication when dealing with fractions: for example, find $\frac{1}{2}$ of 6 means $\frac{1}{2} \times 6$.

If an expression contains only multiplication and division, we evaluate by working from left to right. Similarly, if an expression contains only addition and subtraction, we also evaluate by working from left to right.

WORKED EXAMPLES

1.4   Evaluate

(a) $2 + 3 \times 4$ (b) $(2 + 3) \times 4$

Solution   (a)   Using the BODMAS rule we see that multiplication is carried out first. So

$$2 + 3 \times 4 = 2 + 12 = 14$$

(b)   Using the BODMAS rule we see that the bracketed expression takes priority over all else. Hence

$$(2 + 3) \times 4 = 5 \times 4 = 20$$

1.5   Evaluate

(a) $4 - 2 \div 2$ (b) $1 - 3 + 2 \times 2$

Solution   (a)   Division is carried out before subtraction, and so

$$4 - 2 \div 2 = 4 - \frac{2}{2} = 3$$

(b)   Multiplication is carried out before subtraction or addition:

$$1 - 3 + 2 \times 2 = 1 - 3 + 4 = 2$$

1.6   Evaluate

(a) $(12 \div 4) \times 3$ (b) $12 \div (4 \times 3)$

Solution   Recall that bracketed expressions are evaluated first.

(a) $(12 \div 4) \times 3 = \left(\dfrac{12}{4}\right) \times 3 = 3 \times 3 = 9$

(b) $12 \div (4 \times 3) = 12 \div 12 = 1$

Example 1.6 shows the importance of the position of brackets in an expression.

Self-assessment questions 1.2

1.   State the BODMAS rule used to evaluate expressions.

2.   The position of brackets in an expression is unimportant. True or false?

Exercise 1.2

1.   Evaluate the following expressions:
   (a) $6 - 2 \times 2$ (b) $(6 - 2) \times 2$
   (c) $6 \div 2 - 2$ (d) $(6 \div 2) - 2$
   (e) $6 - 2 + 3 \times 2$ (f) $6 - (2 + 3) \times 2$
   (g) $(6 - 2) + 3 \times 2$ (h) $\dfrac{16}{-2}$ (i) $\dfrac{-24}{-3}$
   (j) $(-6) \times (-2)$ (k) $(-2)(-3)(-4)$

2.   Place brackets in the following expressions to make them correct:
   (a) $6 \times 12 - 3 + 1 = 55$
   (b) $6 \times 12 - 3 + 1 = 68$
   (c) $6 \times 12 - 3 + 1 = 60$
   (d) $5 \times 4 - 3 + 2 = 7$
   (e) $5 \times 4 - 3 + 2 = 15$
   (f) $5 \times 4 - 3 + 2 = -5$

1.3   Prime numbers and factorisation

A **prime number** is a positive integer, larger than 1, which cannot be expressed as the product of two smaller positive integers. To put it another way, a prime number is one that can be divided exactly only by 1 and itself.

For example, $6 = 2 \times 3$, so 6 can be expressed as a product of smaller numbers and hence 6 is not a prime number. However, 7 is prime. Examples of prime numbers are 2, 3, 5, 7, 11, 13, 17, 19, 23. Note that 2 is the only even prime.

Factorise means 'write as a product'. By writing 12 as 3×4 we have factorised 12. We say 3 is a **factor** of 12 and 4 is also a factor of 12. The way in which a number is factorised is not unique: for example, 12 may be expressed as 3×4 or 2×6. Note that 2 and 6 are also factors of 12.

When a number is written as a product of prime numbers we say the number has been **prime factorised.**

To prime factorise a number, consider the technique used in the following examples.

WORKED EXAMPLES

1.7 Prime factorise the following numbers:

(a) 12 (b) 42 (c) 40 (d) 70

Solution (a) We begin with 2 and see whether this is a factor of 12. Clearly it is, so we write

$$12 = 2 \times 6$$

Now we consider 6. Again 2 is a factor so we write

$$12 = 2 \times 2 \times 3$$

All the factors are now prime, that is the prime factorisation of 12 is $2 \times 2 \times 3$.

(b) We begin with 2 and see whether this is a factor of 42. Clearly it is and so we can write

$$42 = 2 \times 21$$

Now we consider 21. Now 2 is not a factor of 21, so we examine the next prime, 3. Clearly 3 is a factor of 21 and so we can write

$$42 = 2 \times 3 \times 7$$

All the factors are now prime, and so the prime factorisation of 42 is $2 \times 3 \times 7$.

(c) Clearly 2 is a factor of 40,

$$40 = 2 \times 20$$

Clearly 2 is a factor of 20,

$$40 = 2 \times 2 \times 10$$

Again 2 is a factor of 10,

$$40 = 2 \times 2 \times 2 \times 5$$

All the factors are now prime. The prime factorisation of 40 is $2 \times 2 \times 2 \times 5$.

(d)   Clearly 2 is a factor of 70,

$$70 = 2 \times 35$$

We consider 35: 2 is not a factor, 3 is not a factor, but 5 is:

$$70 = 2 \times 5 \times 7$$

All the factors are prime. The prime factorisation of 70 is $2 \times 5 \times 7$.

1.8   Prime factorise 2299.

Solution   We note that 2 is not a factor and so we try 3. Again 3 is not a factor and so we try 5. This process continues until we find the first prime factor. It is 11:

$$2299 = 11 \times 209$$

We now consider 209. The first prime factor is 11:

$$2299 = 11 \times 11 \times 19$$

All the factors are prime. The prime factorisation of 2299 is $11 \times 11 \times 19$.

Here we illustrate how software can be used to perform the prime factorisation of 2299 using GeoGebra Classic v6 with the CAS (Computer Algebra System) interface. Numerous other packages are available that perform the same calculation. Figure 1.6 illustrates the output following the command **Factor( )** which performs the prime factorisation. Compare this output to the solution of Worked Example 1.8, particularly the use of the power 2 in 11^2. Powers, or indices as they are also called, are explained in Chapter 5.

Figure 1.6
Syntax used to
perform prime number
calculations.

In addition, Figure 1.6 shows the commands **IsPrime( )** and **NextPrime( )** which will test whether a given number is prime and find the first prime number greater than a given number. You should consult the on-line help provided with your software to explore other prime number commands.

Self-assessment questions 1.3

1. Explain what is meant by a prime number.

2. List the first 10 prime numbers.

3. Explain why all even numbers other than 2 cannot be prime.

Exercise 1.3

1. State which of the following numbers are prime numbers:
   (a) 13   (b) 1000   (c) 2   (d) 29   (e) $\frac{1}{2}$

2. Prime factorise the following numbers:
   (a) 26   (b) 100   (c) 27   (d) 71   (e) 64   (f) 87   (g) 437   (h) 899

3. Prime factorise the two numbers 30 and 42. List any prime factors which are common to both numbers.

1.4   Highest common factor and lowest common multiple

Highest common factor

Suppose we prime factorise 12. This gives $12 = 2 \times 2 \times 3$. From this prime factorisation we can deduce all the factors of 12:

> 2 is a factor of 12
> 3 is a factor of 12
> $2 \times 2 = 4$ is a factor of 12
> $2 \times 3 = 6$ is a factor of 12

Hence 12 has factors 2, 3, 4 and 6, in addition to the obvious factors of 1 and 12.

Similarly we could prime factorise 18 to obtain $18 = 2 \times 3 \times 3$. From this we can list the factors of 18:

> 2 is a factor of 18
> 3 is a factor of 18
> $2 \times 3 = 6$ is a factor of 18
> $3 \times 3 = 9$ is a factor of 18

The factors of 18 are 1, 2, 3, 6, 9 and 18. Some factors are common to both 12 and 18. These are 2, 3 and 6. These are **common factors** of 12 and 18. The highest common factor of 12 and 18 is 6.

The highest common factor of 12 and 18 can be obtained directly from their prime factorisation. We simply note all the primes common to both factorisations:

$$12 = 2 \times 2 \times 3 \qquad 18 = 2 \times 3 \times 3$$

Common to both is 2×3. Thus the highest common factor is $2 \times 3 = 6$. Thus 6 is the highest number that divides exactly into both 12 and 18.

Key point	Given two or more numbers the **highest common factor** (h.c.f.) is the largest (highest) number that is a factor of all the given numbers. The highest common factor is also referred to as the **greatest common divisor** (g.c.d).

WORKED EXAMPLES

1.9   Find the h.c.f. of 12 and 27.

Solution   We prime factorise 12 and 27:

$$12 = 2 \times 2 \times 3 \qquad 27 = 3 \times 3 \times 3$$

Common to both is 3. Thus 3 is the h.c.f. of 12 and 27. This means that 3 is the highest number that divides both 12 and 27.

1.10   Find the h.c.f. of 28 and 210.

Solution   The numbers are prime factorised:

$$28 = 2 \times 2 \times 7$$
$$210 = 2 \times 3 \times 5 \times 7$$

The factors that are common are identified: a 2 is common to both and a 7 is common to both. Hence both numbers are divisible by $2 \times 7 = 14$. Since this number contains all the common factors it is the highest common factor.

1.11   Find the h.c.f. of 90 and 108.

Solution   The numbers are prime factorised:

$$90 = 2 \times 3 \times 3 \times 5$$
$$108 = 2 \times 2 \times 3 \times 3 \times 3$$

The common factors are 2, 3 and 3 and so the h.c.f. is $2 \times 3 \times 3$, that is 18. This is the highest number that divides both 90 and 108.

1.12   Find the h.c.f. of 12, 18 and 20.

Solution   Prime factorisation yields

$$12 = 2 \times 2 \times 3 \qquad 18 = 2 \times 3 \times 3 \qquad 20 = 2 \times 2 \times 5$$

There is only one factor common to all three numbers: it is 2. Hence 2 is the h.c.f. of 12, 18 and 20.

Lowest common multiple

Suppose we are given two or more numbers and wish to find numbers into which all the given numbers will divide. For example, given 4 and 6 we see that they both divide exactly into 12, 24, 36, 48, 60 and so on. The smallest number into which they both divide is 12. We say 12 is the **lowest common multiple** of 4 and 6.

Key point

The lowest common multiple (l.c.m.) of a set of numbers is the smallest (lowest) number into which all the given numbers will divide exactly.

WORKED EXAMPLE

1.13   Find the l.c.m. of 6 and 10.

Solution   We seek the smallest number into which both 6 and 10 will divide exactly. There are many numbers into which 6 and 10 will divide, for example 60, 120, 600, but we are seeking the smallest such number. By inspection, the smallest such number is 30. Thus the l.c.m. of 6 and 10 is 30.

A more systematic method of finding the l.c.m. involves the use of prime factorisation.

WORKED EXAMPLES

1.14   Find the l.c.m. of 15 and 20.

Solution   As a first step, the numbers are prime factorised:

$$15 = 3 \times 5 \qquad 20 = 2 \times 2 \times 5$$

Since 15 must divide into the l.c.m., then the l.c.m. must contain the factors of 15, that is 3×5. Similarly, as 20 must divide into the l.c.m., then the l.c.m. must also contain the factors of 20, that is $2 \times 2 \times 5$. The l.c.m. is the smallest number that contains both of these sets of factors. Note that the l.c.m. will contain only 2s, 3s and 5s as its prime factors. We now need to determine how many of these particular factors are needed.

To determine the l.c.m. we ask 'How many factors of 2 are required?', 'How many factors of 3 are required?', 'How many factors of 5 are required?'

The highest number of 2s occurs in the factorisation of 20. Hence the l.c.m. requires two factors of 2. Consider the number of 3s required. The highest number of 3s occurs in the factorisation of 15. Hence the l.c.m. requires one factor of 3. Consider the number of 5s required. The highest number of 5s is 1 and so the l.c.m. requires one factor of 5. Hence the l.c.m. is $2 \times 2 \times 3 \times 5 = 60$.

Hence 60 is the smallest number into which both 15 and 20 will divide exactly.

1.15   Find the l.c.m. of 20, 24 and 25.

Solution   The numbers are prime factorised:

$$20 = 2 \times 2 \times 5 \qquad 24 = 2 \times 2 \times 2 \times 3 \qquad 25 = 5 \times 5$$

By considering the prime factorisations of 20, 24 and 25 we see that the only primes involved are 2, 3 and 5. Hence the l.c.m. will contain only 2s, 3s and 5s.

Consider the number of 2s required. The highest number of 2s required is three from factorising 24. The highest number of 3s required is one, again from factorising 24. The highest number of 5s required is two, found from factorising 25. Hence the l.c.m. is given by

$$\text{l.c.m.} = 2 \times 2 \times 2 \times 3 \times 5 \times 5 = 600$$

Hence 600 is the smallest number into which 20, 24 and 25 will all divide exactly.

GeoGebra can be used to find the highest common factor, **HCF( )**, and lowest common multiple, **LCM( )**, of a set or list of numbers, entered using braces, for example as **a={12,18,20}**. Use of this software for verification of Worked Examples 1.12 and 1.15 is shown in Figure 1.7.

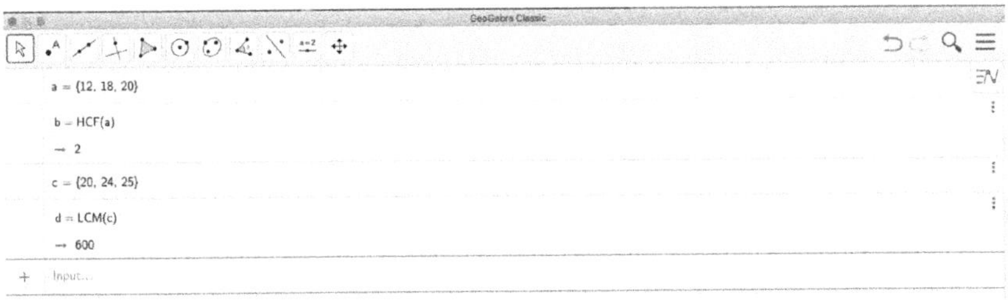

Figure 1.7
Using software to find the h.c.f and l.c.m.

a = {12, 18, 20}

b = HCF(a)

→ 2

c = {20, 24, 25}

d = LCM(c)

→ 600

Self-assessment questions 1.4

1. Explain what is meant by the h.c.f. of a set of numbers.

2. Explain what is meant by the l.c.m. of a set of numbers.

Exercise 1.4

1. Calculate the h.c.f. of the following sets of numbers:
    (a) 12, 15, 21   (b) 16, 24, 40   (c) 28, 70, 120, 160   (d) 35, 38, 42   (e) 96, 120, 144

2. Calculate the l.c.m. of the following sets of numbers:
    (a) 5, 6, 8   (b) 20, 30   (c) 7, 9, 12   (d) 100, 150, 235   (e) 96, 120, 144

Test and assignment exercises 1

1. Evaluate
    (a) $6 \div 2 + 1$
    (b) $6 \div (2 + 1)$
    (c) $12 + 4 \div 4$
    (d) $(12 + 4) \div 4$
    (e) $3 \times 2 + 1$
    (f) $3 \times (2 + 1)$
    (g) $6 - 2 + 4 \div 2$
    (h) $(6 - 2 + 4) \div 2$
    (i) $6 - (2 + 4 \div 2)$
    (j) $6 - (2 + 4) \div 2$
    (k) $2 \times 4 - 1$
    (l) $2 \times (4 - 1)$
    (m) $2 \times 6 \div (3 - 1)$
    (n) $2 \times (6 \div 3) - 1$
    (o) $2 \times (6 \div 3 - 1)$

2. Prime factorise (a) 56, (b) 39, (c) 74.

3. Find the h.c.f. of
    (a) 8, 12, 14   (b) 18, 42, 66   (c) 20, 24, 30   (d) 16, 24, 32, 160

4. Find the l.c.m. of
    (a) 10, 15   (b) 11, 13   (c) 8, 14, 16   (d) 15, 24, 30

Fractions

Objectives: This chapter:

- explains what is meant by a fraction
- defines the terms 'improper fraction', 'proper fraction' and 'mixed fraction'
- explains how to write fractions in different but equivalent forms
- explains how to simplify fractions by cancelling common factors
- explains how to add, subtract, multiply and divide fractions

2.1 Introduction

The arithmetic of fractions is very important groundwork which must be mastered before topics in algebra such as formulae and equations can be understood. The same techniques that are used to manipulate fractions are used in these more advanced topics. You should use this chapter to ensure that you are confident at handling fractions before moving on to algebra. In all the examples and exercises it is important that you should carry out the calculations without the use of a calculator.

Fractions are numbers such as $\frac{1}{2}, \frac{3}{4}, \frac{11}{8}$ and so on. In general a fraction is a number of the form $\frac{p}{q}$, where the letters p and q represent whole numbers or integers. The integer q can never be zero because it is not possible to divide by zero.

In any fraction $\frac{p}{q}$ the number p is called the **numerator** and the number q is called the **denominator.**

Key point

$$\text{fraction} = \frac{\text{numerator}}{\text{denominator}} = \frac{p}{q}$$

Suppose that p and q are both positive numbers. If p is less than q, the fraction is said to be a **proper fraction.** So $\frac{1}{2}$ and $\frac{3}{4}$ are proper fractions since the numerator is less than the denominator. If p is greater than or equal to q, the fraction is said to be **improper.** So $\frac{11}{8}$, $\frac{7}{4}$ and $\frac{3}{3}$ are all improper fractions.

If either of p or q is negative, we simply ignore the negative sign when determining whether the fraction is proper or improper. So $-\frac{3}{5}$, $\frac{-7}{21}$ and $\frac{4}{-21}$ are proper fractions, but $\frac{3}{-3}$, $\frac{-8}{2}$ and $-\frac{11}{2}$ are improper.

Note that all proper fractions have a value less than 1.

The denominator of a fraction can take the value 1, as in $\frac{3}{1}$ and $\frac{7}{1}$. In these cases the result is a whole number, 3 and 7.

A fraction is **inverted** by interchanging its numerator and denominator. When $\frac{3}{2}$ is inverted this results in $\frac{2}{3}$. If 4 is inverted this results in $\frac{1}{4}$ since $4 = \frac{4}{1}$.

The **reciprocal** of a number is found by inverting it, so, for example, the reciprocal of $\frac{4}{5}$ is $\frac{5}{4}$.

Self-assessment questions 2.1

1. Explain the terms (a) fraction, (b) improper fraction, (c) proper fraction. In each case give an example of your own.

2. Explain the terms (a) numerator, (b) denominator.

Exercise 2.1

1. Classify each of the following as proper or improper:
   (a) $\frac{9}{17}$ (b) $\frac{-9}{17}$ (c) $\frac{8}{8}$ (d) $-\frac{7}{8}$ (e) $\frac{110}{77}$

2.2   Expressing a fraction in equivalent forms

Given a fraction, we may be able to express it in a different form. For example, you will know that $\frac{1}{2}$ is equivalent to $\frac{2}{4}$. Note that multiplying both numerator and denominator by the same number leaves the value of the fraction unchanged. So, for example,

$$\frac{1}{2} = \frac{1 \times 2}{2 \times 2} = \frac{2}{4}$$

We say that $\frac{1}{2}$ and $\frac{2}{4}$ are **equivalent fractions.** Although they might look different, they have the same value.

Similarly, given the fraction $\frac{8}{12}$ we can divide both numerator and denominator by 4 to obtain

$$\frac{8}{12} = \frac{8/4}{12/4} = \frac{2}{3}$$

so $\frac{8}{12}$ and $\frac{2}{3}$ have the same value and are equivalent fractions.

| **Key point** | Multiplying or dividing both numerator and denominator of a fraction by the same number produces a fraction having the same value, called an equivalent fraction. |

A fraction is in its **simplest form** when there are no factors common to both numerator and denominator. For example, $\frac{5}{12}$ is in its simplest form, but $\frac{3}{6}$ is not since 3 is a factor common to both numerator and denominator. Its simplest form is the equivalent fraction $\frac{1}{2}$.

To express a fraction in its simplest form we look for factors that are common to both the numerator and denominator. This is done by prime factorising both of these. Dividing both the numerator and denominator by any common factors removes them but leaves an equivalent fraction. This is equivalent to cancelling any common factors. For example, to simplify $\frac{4}{6}$ we prime factorise to produce

$$\frac{4}{6} = \frac{2 \times 2}{2 \times 3}$$

Dividing both numerator and denominator by 2 leaves $\frac{2}{3}$. This is equivalent to cancelling the common factor of 2.

WORKED EXAMPLES

2.1   Express $\frac{24}{36}$ in its simplest form.

Solution   We seek factors common to both numerator and denominator. To do this we prime factorise 24 and 36:

Prime factorisation has been described in §1.3.

$$24 = 2 \times 2 \times 2 \times 3 \qquad 36 = 2 \times 2 \times 3 \times 3$$

The factors $2 \times 2 \times 3$ are common to both 24 and 36 and so these may be cancelled. Note that only common factors may be cancelled when simplifying a fraction. Hence

Finding the highest common factor (h.c.f.) of two numbers is detailed in §1.4.

$$\frac{24}{36} = \frac{2 \times 2 \times 2 \times 3}{2 \times 2 \times 3 \times 3} = \frac{2}{3}$$

In its simplest form $\frac{24}{36}$ is $\frac{2}{3}$. In effect we have divided 24 and 36 by 12, which is their h.c.f.

2.2   Express $\frac{49}{21}$ in its simplest form.

Solution   Prime factorising 49 and 21 gives

$$49 = 7 \times 7 \qquad 21 = 3 \times 7$$

Their h.c.f. is 7. Dividing 49 and 21 by 7 gives

$$\frac{49}{21} = \frac{7}{3}$$

Hence the simplest form of $\frac{49}{21}$ is $\frac{7}{3}$.

Before we can start to add and subtract fractions it is necessary to be able to convert fractions into a variety of equivalent forms. Work through the following examples.

WORKED EXAMPLES

2.3   Express $\frac{3}{4}$ as an equivalent fraction having a denominator of 20.

Solution   To achieve a denominator of 20, the existing denominator must be multiplied by 5. To produce an equivalent fraction both numerator and denominator must be multiplied by 5, so

$$\frac{3}{4} = \frac{3 \times 5}{4 \times 5} = \frac{15}{20}$$

2.4   Express 7 as an equivalent fraction with a denominator of 3.

Solution   Note that 7 is the same as the fraction $\frac{7}{1}$. To achieve a denominator of 3, the existing denominator must be multiplied by 3. To produce an equivalent fraction both numerator and denominator must be multiplied by 3, so

$$7 = \frac{7}{1} = \frac{7 \times 3}{1 \times 3} = \frac{21}{3}$$

Self-assessment questions 2.2

1. All integers can be thought of as fractions. True or false?

2. Explain the use of h.c.f. in the simplification of fractions.

3. Give an example of three fractions that are equivalent.

Exercise 2.2

1. Express the following fractions in their simplest form:
   (a) $\frac{18}{27}$ (b) $\frac{12}{20}$ (c) $\frac{15}{45}$ (d) $\frac{25}{80}$ (e) $\frac{15}{60}$
   (f) $\frac{90}{200}$ (g) $\frac{15}{20}$ (h) $\frac{2}{18}$ (i) $\frac{16}{24}$ (j) $\frac{30}{65}$
   (k) $\frac{12}{21}$ (l) $\frac{100}{45}$ (m) $\frac{6}{9}$ (n) $\frac{12}{16}$ (o) $\frac{13}{42}$
   (p) $\frac{13}{39}$ (q) $\frac{11}{33}$ (r) $\frac{14}{30}$ (s) $-\frac{12}{16}$ (t) $\frac{11}{-33}$
   (u) $\frac{-14}{-30}$

2. Express $\frac{3}{4}$ as an equivalent fraction having a denominator of 28.

3. Express 4 as an equivalent fraction with a denominator of 5.

4. Express $\frac{5}{12}$ as an equivalent fraction having a denominator of 36.

5. Express 2 as an equivalent fraction with a denominator of 4.

6. Express 6 as an equivalent fraction with a denominator of 3.

7. Express each of the fractions $\frac{2}{3}, \frac{5}{4}$ and $\frac{5}{6}$ as an equivalent fraction with a denominator of 12.

8. Express each of the fractions $\frac{4}{9}, \frac{1}{2}$ and $\frac{5}{6}$ as an equivalent fraction with a denominator of 18.

9. Express each of the following numbers as an equivalent fraction with a denominator of 12:
   (a) $\frac{1}{2}$ (b) $\frac{3}{4}$ (c) $\frac{5}{2}$ (d) 5   (e) 4   (f) 12

2.3   Addition and subtraction of fractions

To add and subtract fractions we first rewrite each fraction so that they all have the same denominator. This is known as the **common denominator.** The denominator is chosen to be the lowest common multiple of the original denominators. Then the numerators only are added or subtracted as appropriate, and the result is divided by the common denominator.

WORKED EXAMPLES

2.5   Find $\frac{2}{3} + \frac{5}{4}$.

Solution   The denominators are 3 and 4. The l.c.m. of 3 and 4 is 12. We need to express both fractions with a denominator of 12.

Finding the lowest common multiple (l.c.m.) is detailed in §1.4.

To express $\frac{2}{3}$ with a denominator of 12 we multiply both numerator and denominator by 4. Hence $\frac{2}{3}$ is the same as $\frac{8}{12}$. To express $\frac{5}{4}$ with a denominator of 12 we multiply both numerator and denominator by 3. Hence $\frac{5}{4}$ is the same as $\frac{15}{12}$. So

$$\frac{2}{3} + \frac{5}{4} = \frac{8}{12} + \frac{15}{12} = \frac{8 + 15}{12} = \frac{23}{12}$$

2.6   Find $\frac{4}{9} - \frac{1}{2} + \frac{5}{6}$.

Solution   The denominators are 9, 2 and 6. Their l.c.m. is 18. Each fraction is expressed with 18 as the denominator:

$$\frac{4}{9} = \frac{8}{18} \qquad \frac{1}{2} = \frac{9}{18} \qquad \frac{5}{6} = \frac{15}{18}$$

Then

$$\frac{4}{9} - \frac{1}{2} + \frac{5}{6} = \frac{8}{18} - \frac{9}{18} + \frac{15}{18} = \frac{8 - 9 + 15}{18} = \frac{14}{18}$$

The fraction $\frac{14}{18}$ can be simplified to $\frac{7}{9}$. Hence

$$\frac{4}{9} - \frac{1}{2} + \frac{5}{6} = \frac{7}{9}$$

2.7   Find $\frac{1}{4} - \frac{5}{9}$.

Solution   The l.c.m. of 4 and 9 is 36. Each fraction is expressed with a denominator of 36. Thus

$$\frac{1}{4} = \frac{9}{36} \quad \text{and} \quad \frac{5}{9} = \frac{20}{36}$$

Then

$$\frac{1}{4} - \frac{5}{9} = \frac{9}{36} - \frac{20}{36}$$

$$= \frac{9 - 20}{36}$$

$$= \frac{-11}{36}$$

$$= -\frac{11}{36}$$

Consider the number $2\frac{3}{4}$. This is referred to as a **mixed fraction** because it contains a whole number part, 2, and a fractional part, $\frac{3}{4}$. We can convert this mixed fraction into an improper fraction as follows. Recognise that 2 is equivalent to $\frac{8}{4}$, and so $2\frac{3}{4}$ is $\frac{8}{4} + \frac{3}{4} = \frac{11}{4}$.

The reverse of this process is to convert an improper fraction into a mixed fraction. Consider the improper fraction $\frac{11}{4}$. We seek the largest multiple of the denominator that is less than the numerator. The numerator is then split into

Numerator = Multiple of denominator + Remainder

In this example, the numerator is 11, the denominator is 4. So the largest multiple of 4 that is less than 11 is $2 \times 4 = 8$. So we write

$$11 = 8 + \text{Remainder} = 8 + 3$$

Then

$$\frac{11}{4} = \frac{8 + 3}{4} = \frac{8}{4} + \frac{3}{4} = 2 + \frac{3}{4} = 2\frac{3}{4}$$

WORKED EXAMPLE

2.8   (a) Express $4\frac{2}{5}$ as an improper fraction.

(b) Find $4\frac{2}{5} + \frac{1}{3}$.

(c) Convert to mixed fractions i. $\frac{38}{5}$ ii. $\frac{118}{7}$

Solution   (a) $4\frac{2}{5}$ is a mixed fraction. Note that $4\frac{2}{5}$ is equal to $4 + \frac{2}{5}$. We can write 4 as the equivalent fraction $\frac{20}{5}$. Therefore

$$4\frac{2}{5} = \frac{20}{5} + \frac{2}{5}$$

$$= \frac{22}{5}$$

(b) $\quad 4\dfrac{2}{5} + \dfrac{1}{3} = \dfrac{22}{5} + \dfrac{1}{3}$

$$= \dfrac{66}{15} + \dfrac{5}{15}$$

$$= \dfrac{71}{15}$$

(c) i. The largest multiple of 5 that is less than 38 is $7 \times 5 = 35$. So we write $38 = 35 + 3$ and then

$$\dfrac{38}{5} = \dfrac{35 + 3}{5} = \dfrac{35}{5} + \dfrac{3}{5} = 7 + \dfrac{3}{5} = 7\dfrac{3}{5}$$

ii. The largest multiple of 7 that is less than 118 is $7 \times 16 = 112$. Hence we write $118 = 112 + 6$. Then

$$\dfrac{118}{7} = \dfrac{112}{7} + \dfrac{6}{7} = 16 + \dfrac{6}{7} = 16\dfrac{6}{7}$$

Self-assessment question 2.3

1. Explain the use of l.c.m. when adding and subtracting fractions.

Exercise 2.3

1. Find

(a) $\dfrac{1}{4} + \dfrac{2}{3}$ (b) $\dfrac{3}{5} + \dfrac{5}{3}$ (c) $\dfrac{12}{14} - \dfrac{2}{7}$

(d) $\dfrac{3}{7} - \dfrac{1}{2} + \dfrac{2}{21}$ (e) $1\dfrac{1}{2} + \dfrac{4}{9}$

(f) $2\dfrac{1}{4} - 1\dfrac{1}{3} + \dfrac{1}{2}$ (g) $\dfrac{10}{15} - 1\dfrac{2}{5} + \dfrac{8}{3}$

(h) $\dfrac{9}{10} - \dfrac{7}{16} + \dfrac{1}{2} - \dfrac{2}{5}$

2. Find

(a) $\dfrac{7}{8} + \dfrac{1}{3}$ (b) $\dfrac{1}{2} - \dfrac{3}{4}$ (c) $\dfrac{3}{5} + \dfrac{2}{3} + \dfrac{1}{2}$

(d) $\dfrac{3}{8} + \dfrac{1}{3} + \dfrac{1}{4}$ (e) $\dfrac{2}{3} - \dfrac{4}{7}$ (f) $\dfrac{1}{11} - \dfrac{1}{2}$

(g) $\dfrac{3}{11} - \dfrac{5}{8}$

3. Express as improper fractions:

(a) $2\dfrac{1}{2}$ (b) $3\dfrac{2}{3}$ (c) $10\dfrac{1}{4}$ (d) $5\dfrac{2}{7}$

(e) $6\dfrac{2}{9}$ (f) $11\dfrac{1}{3}$ (g) $15\dfrac{1}{2}$ (h) $13\dfrac{3}{4}$

(i) $12\dfrac{1}{11}$ (j) $13\dfrac{2}{3}$ (k) $56\dfrac{1}{2}$

4. Without using a calculator express these improper fractions as mixed fractions:

(a) $\dfrac{10}{3}$ (b) $\dfrac{7}{2}$ (c) $\dfrac{15}{4}$ (d) $\dfrac{25}{6}$

2.4   Multiplication of fractions

The product of two or more fractions is found by multiplying their numerators to form a new numerator, and then multiplying their denominators to form a new denominator.

WORKED EXAMPLES

2.9   Find $\frac{4}{9} \times \frac{3}{8}$.

Solution   The numerators are multiplied: $4 \times 3 = 12$. The denominators are multiplied: $9 \times 8 = 72$. Hence

$$\frac{4}{9} \times \frac{3}{8} = \frac{12}{72}$$

This may now be expressed in its simplest form:

$$\frac{12}{72} = \frac{1}{6}$$

Hence

$$\frac{4}{9} \times \frac{3}{8} = \frac{1}{6}$$

An alternative, but equivalent, method is to cancel any factors common to both numerator and denominator at the outset:

$$\frac{4}{9} \times \frac{3}{8} = \frac{4 \times 3}{9 \times 8}$$

A factor of 4 is common to the 4 and the 8. Hence

$$\frac{4 \times 3}{9 \times 8} = \frac{1 \times 3}{9 \times 2}$$

A factor of 3 is common to the 3 and the 9. Hence

$$\frac{1 \times 3}{9 \times 2} = \frac{1 \times 1}{3 \times 2} = \frac{1}{6}$$

2.10   Find $\frac{12}{25} \times \frac{2}{7} \times \frac{10}{9}$.

Solution   We cancel factors common to both numerator and denominator. A factor of 5 is common to 10 and 25. Cancelling this gives

$$\frac{12}{25} \times \frac{2}{7} \times \frac{10}{9} = \frac{12}{5} \times \frac{2}{7} \times \frac{2}{9}$$

A factor of 3 is common to 12 and 9. Cancelling this gives

$$\frac{12}{5} \times \frac{2}{7} \times \frac{2}{9} = \frac{4}{5} \times \frac{2}{7} \times \frac{2}{3}$$

There are no more common factors. Hence

$$\frac{12}{25} \times \frac{2}{7} \times \frac{10}{9} = \frac{4}{5} \times \frac{2}{7} \times \frac{2}{3} = \frac{16}{105}$$

2.11 Find $\frac{3}{4}$ of $\frac{5}{9}$.

Recall that 'of' means multiply.

Solution $\frac{3}{4}$ of $\frac{5}{9}$ is the same as $\frac{3}{4} \times \frac{5}{9}$. Cancelling a factor of 3 from numerator and denominator gives $\frac{1}{4} \times \frac{5}{3}$, that is $\frac{5}{12}$. Hence $\frac{3}{4}$ of $\frac{5}{9}$ is $\frac{5}{12}$.

2.12 Find $\frac{5}{6}$ of 70.

Solution We can write 70 as $\frac{70}{1}$. So

$$\frac{5}{6} \text{ of } 70 = \frac{5}{6} \times \frac{70}{1} = \frac{5}{3} \times \frac{35}{1} = \frac{175}{3} = 58\frac{1}{3}$$

2.13 Find $2\frac{7}{8} \times \frac{2}{3}$.

Solution In this example the first fraction is a mixed fraction. We convert it to an improper fraction before performing the multiplication. Note that $2\frac{7}{8} = \frac{23}{8}$. Then

$$\frac{23}{8} \times \frac{2}{3} = \frac{23}{4} \times \frac{1}{3}$$

$$= \frac{23}{12}$$

$$= 1\frac{11}{12}$$

Self-assessment question 2.4

1. Describe how to multiply fractions together.

Exercise 2.4

1. Evaluate

   (a) $\frac{2}{3} \times \frac{6}{7}$ (b) $\frac{8}{15} \times \frac{25}{32}$ (c) $\frac{1}{4} \times \frac{8}{9}$

   (d) $\frac{16}{17} \times \frac{34}{48}$ (e) $2 \times \frac{3}{5} \times \frac{5}{12}$

   (f) $2\frac{1}{3} \times 1\frac{1}{4}$ (g) $1\frac{3}{4} \times 2\frac{1}{2}$

   (h) $\frac{3}{4} \times 1\frac{1}{2} \times 3\frac{1}{2}$

2. Evaluate

   (a) $\frac{2}{3}$ of $\frac{3}{4}$ (b) $\frac{4}{7}$ of $\frac{21}{30}$

   (c) $\frac{9}{10}$ of 80   (d) $\frac{6}{7}$ of 42

3. Is $\frac{3}{4}$ of $\frac{12}{15}$ the same as $\frac{12}{15}$ of $\frac{3}{4}$?

4. Find

(a) $-\dfrac{1}{3} \times \dfrac{5}{7}$ (b) $\dfrac{3}{4} \times -\dfrac{1}{2}$

(c) $\left(-\dfrac{5}{8}\right) \times \dfrac{8}{11}$ (d) $\left(-\dfrac{2}{3}\right) \times \left(-\dfrac{15}{7}\right)$

5. Find

(a) $5\dfrac{1}{2} \times \dfrac{1}{2}$ (b) $3\dfrac{3}{4} \times \dfrac{1}{3}$ (c) $\dfrac{2}{3} \times 5\dfrac{1}{9}$

(d) $\dfrac{3}{4} \times 11\dfrac{1}{2}$

6. Find

(a) $\dfrac{3}{5}$ of $11\dfrac{1}{4}$ (b) $\dfrac{2}{3}$ of $15\dfrac{1}{2}$

(c) $\dfrac{1}{4}$ of $-8\dfrac{1}{3}$

2.5   Division by a fraction

To divide one fraction by another fraction, we invert the second fraction and then multiply. When we invert a fraction we interchange the numerator and denominator.

WORKED EXAMPLES

2.14   Find $\dfrac{6}{25} \div \dfrac{2}{5}$.

Solution   We invert $\dfrac{2}{5}$ to obtain $\dfrac{5}{2}$. Multiplication is then performed. So

$$\frac{6}{25} \div \frac{2}{5} = \frac{6}{25} \times \frac{5}{2} = \frac{3}{25} \times \frac{5}{1} = \frac{3}{5} \times \frac{1}{1} = \frac{3}{5}$$

2.15   Evaluate (a) $1\dfrac{1}{3} \div \dfrac{8}{3}$,   (b) $\dfrac{20}{21} \div \dfrac{5}{7}$.

Solution   (a)   First we express $1\frac{1}{3}$ as an improper fraction:

$$1\frac{1}{3} = 1 + \frac{1}{3} = \frac{3}{3} + \frac{1}{3} = \frac{4}{3}$$

So we calculate

$$\frac{4}{3} \div \frac{8}{3} = \frac{4}{3} \times \frac{3}{8} = \frac{4}{8} = \frac{1}{2}$$

Hence

$$1\frac{1}{3} \div \frac{8}{3} = \frac{1}{2}$$

(b) $$\frac{20}{21} \div \frac{5}{7} = \frac{20}{21} \times \frac{7}{5} = \frac{4}{21} \times \frac{7}{1} = \frac{4}{3}$$

Self-assessment question 2.5

1. Explain the process of division by a fraction.

Exercise 2.5

1. Evaluate

(a) $\dfrac{3}{4} \div \dfrac{1}{8}$

(b) $\dfrac{8}{9} \div \dfrac{4}{3}$

(c) $\dfrac{-2}{7} \div \dfrac{4}{21}$

(d) $\dfrac{9}{4} \div 1\dfrac{1}{2}$

(e) $\dfrac{5}{6} \div \dfrac{5}{12}$

(f) $\dfrac{99}{100} \div 1\dfrac{4}{5}$

(g) $3\dfrac{1}{4} \div 1\dfrac{1}{8}$

(h) $\left(2\dfrac{1}{4} \div \dfrac{3}{4}\right) \times 2$

(i) $2\dfrac{1}{4} \div \left(\dfrac{3}{4} \times 2\right)$

(j) $6\dfrac{1}{4} \div 2\dfrac{1}{2} + 5$

(k) $6\dfrac{1}{4} \div \left(2\dfrac{1}{2} + 5\right)$

Test and assignment exercises 2

1. Evaluate

(a) $\dfrac{3}{4} + \dfrac{1}{6}$

(b) $\dfrac{2}{3} + \dfrac{3}{5} - \dfrac{1}{6}$

(c) $\dfrac{5}{7} - \dfrac{2}{3}$

(d) $2\dfrac{1}{3} - \dfrac{9}{10}$

(e) $5\dfrac{1}{4} + 3\dfrac{1}{6}$

(f) $\dfrac{9}{8} - \dfrac{7}{6} + 1$

(g) $\dfrac{5}{6} - \dfrac{5}{3} + \dfrac{5}{4}$

(h) $\dfrac{4}{5} + \dfrac{1}{3} - \dfrac{3}{4}$

2. Evaluate

(a) $\dfrac{4}{7} \times \dfrac{21}{32}$

(b) $\dfrac{5}{6} \times \dfrac{8}{15}$

(c) $\dfrac{3}{11} \times \dfrac{20}{21}$

(d) $\dfrac{9}{14} \times \dfrac{8}{18}$

(e) $\dfrac{5}{4} \div \dfrac{10}{13}$

(f) $\dfrac{7}{16} \div \dfrac{21}{32}$

(g) $\dfrac{-24}{25} \div \dfrac{51}{50}$

(h) $\dfrac{45}{81} \div \dfrac{25}{27}$

3. Evaluate the following expressions using the BODMAS rule:

(a) $\dfrac{1}{2} + \dfrac{1}{3} \times 2$

(b) $\dfrac{3}{4} \times \dfrac{2}{3} + \dfrac{1}{4}$

(c) $\dfrac{5}{6} \div \dfrac{2}{3} + \dfrac{3}{4}$

(d) $\left(\dfrac{2}{3} + \dfrac{1}{4}\right) \div 4 + \dfrac{3}{5}$

(e) $\left(\dfrac{4}{3} - \dfrac{2}{5} \times \dfrac{1}{3}\right) \times \dfrac{1}{4} + \dfrac{1}{2}$

(f) $\dfrac{3}{4}$ of $\left(1 + \dfrac{2}{3}\right)$

(g) $\dfrac{2}{3}$ of $\dfrac{1}{2} + 1$

(h) $\dfrac{1}{5} \times \dfrac{2}{3} + \dfrac{2}{5} \div \dfrac{4}{5}$

4. Express in their simplest form:

(a) $\dfrac{21}{84}$

(b) $\dfrac{6}{80}$

(c) $\dfrac{34}{85}$

(d) $\dfrac{22}{143}$

(e) $\dfrac{69}{253}$

Decimal numbers

Objectives: This chapter:

- revises the decimal number system
- shows how to write a number to a given number of significant figures
- shows how to write a number to a given number of decimal places

3.1 Decimal numbers

Consider the whole number 478. We can regard it as the sum

$$400 + 70 + 8$$

In this way we see that, in the number 478, the 8 represents eight ones, or 8 units, the 7 represents seven tens, or 70, and the number 4 represents four hundreds or 400. Thus we have the system of hundreds, tens and units familiar from early years in school. All whole numbers can be thought of in this way.

When we wish to deal with proper fractions and mixed fractions, we extend the hundreds, tens and units system as follows. A **decimal point, '.',** marks the end of the whole number part, and the numbers that follow it, to the right, form the fractional part.

A number immediately to the right of the decimal point, that is in the **first decimal place,** represents tenths, so

$$0.1 = \frac{1}{10}$$

$$0.2 = \frac{2}{10} \quad \text{or} \quad \frac{1}{5}$$

$$0.3 = \frac{3}{10} \quad \text{and so on}$$

Note that when there are no whole numbers involved it is usual to write a zero in front of the decimal point, thus, .2 would be written 0.2.

3.1 Express the following decimal numbers as proper fractions in their simplest form

(a) 0.4   (b) 0.5   (c) 0.6

Solution The first number after the decimal point represents tenths.

(a) $0.4 = \frac{4}{10}$, which simplifies to $\frac{2}{5}$

(b) $0.5 = \frac{5}{10}$ or simply $\frac{1}{2}$

(c) $0.6 = \frac{6}{10} = \frac{3}{5}$

Frequently we will deal with numbers having a whole number part and a fractional part. Thus

$$5.2 = 5 \text{ units} + 2 \text{ tenths}$$

$$= 5 + \frac{2}{10}$$

$$= 5 + \frac{1}{5}$$

$$= 5\frac{1}{5}$$

Similarly,

$$175.8 = 175\frac{8}{10} = 175\frac{4}{5}$$

Numbers in the second position after the decimal point, or the **second decimal place,** represent hundredths, so

$$0.01 = \frac{1}{100}$$

$$0.02 = \frac{2}{100} \quad \text{or} \quad \frac{1}{50}$$

$$0.03 = \frac{3}{100} \quad \text{and so on}$$

Consider 0.25. We can think of this as

$$0.25 = 0.2 + 0.05$$

$$= \frac{2}{10} + \frac{5}{100}$$

$$= \frac{25}{100}$$

We see that 0.25 is equivalent to $\frac{25}{100}$, which in its simplest form is $\frac{1}{4}$.

In fact we can regard any numbers occupying the first two decimal places as hundredths, so that

$$0.25 = \frac{25}{100} \quad \text{or simply} \quad \frac{1}{4}$$

$$0.50 = \frac{50}{100} \quad \text{or} \quad \frac{1}{2}$$

$$0.75 = \frac{75}{100} = \frac{3}{4}$$

WORKED EXAMPLES

3.2   Express the following decimal numbers as proper fractions in their simplest form:

(a) 0.35   (b) 0.56   (c) 0.68

Solution   The first two decimal places represent hundredths:

(a) $0.35 = \frac{35}{100} = \frac{7}{20}$

(b) $0.56 = \frac{56}{100} = \frac{14}{25}$

(c) $0.68 = \frac{68}{100} = \frac{17}{25}$

3.3   Express 37.25 as a mixed fraction in its simplest form.

Solution $37.25 = 37 + 0.25$

$$= 37 + \frac{25}{100}$$

$$= 37 + \frac{1}{4}$$

$$= 37\frac{1}{4}$$

Numbers in the third position after the decimal point, or **third decimal place**, represent thousandths, so

$$0.001 = \frac{1}{1000}$$

$$0.002 = \frac{2}{1000} \quad \text{or} \quad \frac{1}{500}$$

$$0.003 = \frac{3}{1000} \quad \text{and so on}$$

In fact we can regard any numbers occupying the first three positions after the decimal point as thousandths, so that

$$0.356 = \frac{356}{1000} \quad \text{or} \quad \frac{89}{250}$$

$$0.015 = \frac{15}{1000} \quad \text{or} \quad \frac{3}{200}$$

$$0.075 = \frac{75}{1000} = \frac{3}{40}$$

WORKED EXAMPLE

3.4   Write each of the following as a decimal number:

(a) $\frac{3}{10} + \frac{7}{100}$ (b) $\frac{8}{10} + \frac{3}{1000}$

Solution

(a) $\frac{3}{10} + \frac{7}{100} = 0.3 + 0.07 = 0.37$

(b) $\frac{8}{10} + \frac{3}{1000} = 0.8 + 0.003 = 0.803$

You will normally use a calculator to add, subtract, multiply and divide decimal numbers. Generally the more decimal places used, the more precisely we can state a number. This idea is developed in the next section.

Self-assessment questions 3.1

1. State which is the largest and which is the smallest of the following numbers:
   23.001, 23.0, 23.00001, 23.0008, 23.01

2. Which is the largest of the following numbers?
   0.1, 0.02, 0.003, 0.0004, 0.00005

Exercise 3.1

1. Express the following decimal numbers as proper fractions in their simplest form:
   (a) 0.7   (b) 0.8   (c) 0.9

2. Express the following decimal numbers as proper fractions in their simplest form:
   (a) 0.55   (b) 0.158   (c) 0.98   (d) 0.099

3. Express each of the following as a mixed fraction in its simplest form:
   (a) 4.6   (b) 5.2   (c) 8.05   (d) 11.59
   (e) 121.09

4. Write each of the following as a decimal number:
   (a) $\frac{6}{10} + \frac{9}{100} + \frac{7}{1000}$ (b) $\frac{8}{100} + \frac{3}{1000}$
   (c) $\frac{17}{1000} + \frac{5}{10}$

3.2   Significant figures and decimal places

The precision to which we state a number often depends upon the context in which the number is being used. The volume of a petrol tank is usually given to the nearest litre. It is of no practical use to give such a volume to the nearest cubic centimetre.

When writing a number we often give the precision by stating the **number of significant figures** or the **number of decimal places** used. These terms are now explained.

Significant figures

Suppose we are asked to write down the number nearest to 857 using at most two non-zero digits, or numbers. We would write 860. This number is nearer to 857 than any other number with two non-zero digits. We say that 857 to 2 **significant figures** is 860. The words 'significant figures' are usually abbreviated to s.f. Because 860 is larger than 857 we say that the 857 has been **rounded up** to 860.

To write a number to three significant figures we can use no more than three non-zero digits. For example, the number closest to 1784 which has no more than three non-zero digits is 1780. We say that 1784 to 3 significant figures is 1780. In this case, because 1780 is less than 1784 we say that 1784 has been **rounded down** to 1780.

WORKED EXAMPLES

3.5   Write down the number nearest to 86 using only one non-zero digit. Has 86 been rounded up or down?

Solution   The number 86 written to one significant figure is 90. This number is nearer to 86 than any other number having only one non-zero digit. Thus 86 has been rounded up to 90.

3.6   Write down the number nearest to 999 which uses only one non-zero digit.

Solution   The number 999 to one significant figure is 1000. This number is nearer to 999 than any other number having only one non-zero digit.

We now explain the process of writing to a given number of significant figures.

When asked to write a number to, say, three significant figures, 3 s.f., the first step is to look at the first four digits. If asked to write a number to two significant figures we look at the first three digits and so on. We always look at one more digit than the number of significant figures required.

For example, to write 6543.19 to 2 s.f. we would consider the number 6540.00; the digits 3, 1 and 9 are effectively ignored. The next step is to round up or down. If the final digit is a 5 or more then we round up by increasing the previous digit by 1. If the final digit is 4 or less we round down by leaving the previous digit unchanged. Hence when considering 6543.19 to 2 s.f., the 4 in the third place means that we round down to 6500.

To write 23865 to 3 s.f. we would consider the number 23860. The next step is to increase the 8 to a 9. Thus 23865 is rounded up to 23900.

Zeros at the beginning of a number are ignored. To write 0.004693 to 2 s.f. we would first consider the number 0.00469. Note that the zeros at the beginning of the number have not been counted. We then round the 6 to a 7, producing 0.0047.

The following examples illustrate the process.

WORKED EXAMPLES

3.7   Write 36.482 to 3 s.f.

Solution   We consider the first four digits, that is 36.48. The final digit is 8 and so we round up 36.48 to 36.5. To 3 s.f. 36.482 is 36.5.

3.8   Write 1.0049 to 4 s.f.

Solution   To write to 4 s.f. we consider the first five digits, that is 1.0049. The final digit is a 9 and so 1.0049 is rounded up to 1.005.

3.9   Write 695.3 to 2 s.f.

Solution   We consider 695. The final digit is a 5 and so we round up. We cannot round up the 9 to a 10 and so the 69 is rounded up to 70. Hence to 2 s.f. the number is 700.

3.10   Write 0.0473 to 1 s.f.

Solution   We do not count the initial zeros and consider 0.047. The final digit tells us to round up. Hence to 1 s.f. we have 0.05.

3.11   A number is given to 2 s.f. as 67.

(a) What is the maximum value the number could have?

(b) What is the minimum value the number could have?

Solution   (a) To 2 s.f. 67.5 is 68. Any number just below 67.5, for example 67.49 or 67.499, to 2 s.f. is 67. Hence the maximum value of the number is 67.4999. . . .

(b) To 2 s.f. 66.4999. . . is 66. However, 66.5 to 2 s.f. is 67. The minimum value of the number is thus 66.5.

Decimal places

When asked to write a number to 3 decimal places (3 d.p.) we consider the first 4 decimal places, that is numbers after the decimal point. If asked to write to 2 d.p. we consider the first 3 decimal places and so on. If the final digit is 5 or more we round up, otherwise we round down.

WORKED EXAMPLES

3.12   Write 63.4261 to 2 d.p.

Solution   We consider the number to 3 d.p., that is 63.426. The final digit is 6 and so we round up 63.426 to 63.43. Hence 63.4261 to 2 d.p. is 63.43.

3.13   Write 1.97 to 1 d.p.

Solution   In order to write to 1 d.p. we consider the number to 2 d.p., that is we consider 1.97. The final digit is a 7 and so we round up. The 9 cannot be rounded up and so we look at 1.9. This can be rounded up to 2.0. Hence 1.97 to 1 d.p. is 2.0. Note that it is crucial to write 2.0 and not simply 2, as this shows that the number is written to 1 d.p.

3.14   Write −6.0439 to 2 d.p.

Solution   We consider −6.043. As the final digit is a 3 the number is rounded down to −6.04.

Self-assessment questions 3.2

1. Explain the meaning of 'significant figures'.

2. Explain the process of writing a number to so many decimal places.

Exercise 3.2

1. Write to 3 s.f.
   (a) 6962   (b) 70.406   (c) 0.0123
   (d) 0.010991   (e) 45.607   (f) 2345

2. Write 65.999 to
   (a) 4 s.f.   (b) 3 s.f.   (c) 2 s.f.
   (d) 1 s.f.   (e) 2 d.p.   (f) 1 d.p.

3. Write 9.99 to
   (a) 1 s.f.   (b) 1 d.p.

4. Write 65.4555 to
   (a) 3 d.p.   (b) 2 d.p.   (c) 1 d.p.
   (d) 5 s.f.   (e) 4 s.f.   (f) 3 s.f.   (g) 2 s.f.
   (h) 1 s.f.

Test and assignment exercises 3

1. Express the following numbers as proper fractions in their simplest form:
   (a) 0.74   (b) 0.96   (c) 0.05   (d) 0.25

2. Express each of the following as a mixed fraction in its simplest form:
   (a) 2.5   (b) 3.25   (c) 3.125   (d) 6.875

3. Write each of the following as a decimal number:
   (a) $\frac{3}{10} + \frac{1}{100} + \frac{7}{1000}$ (b) $\frac{5}{1000} + \frac{9}{100}$ (c) $\frac{4}{1000} + \frac{9}{10}$

4. Write 0.09846 to (a) 1 d.p, (b) 2 s.f., (c) 1 s.f.

5. Write 9.513 to (a) 3 s.f., (b) 2 s.f., (c) 1 s.f.

6. Write 19.96 to (a) 1 d.p., (b) 2 s.f., (c) 1 s.f.

Percentage and ratio

4

Objectives: This chapter:

- explains the terms 'percentage' and 'ratio'
- shows how to perform calculations using percentages and ratios
- explains how to calculate the percentage change in a quantity

4.1 Percentage

In everyday life we come across percentages regularly. During sales periods shops offer discounts – for example, we might hear expressions like 'everything reduced by 50%'. Students often receive examination marks in the form of percentages – for example, to achieve a pass grade in a university examination, a student may be required to score at least 40%. Banks and building societies charge interest on loans, and the interest rate quoted is usually given as a percentage, for example 4.75%. Percentages also provide a way of comparing two or more quantities. For example, suppose we want to know which is the better mark: 40 out of 70, or 125 out of 200? By expressing these marks as percentages we will be able to answer this question.

Consequently an understanding of what a percentage is, and an ability to perform calculations involving percentages, are not only useful in mathematical applications, but also essential life skills.

Fundamentally, a **percentage** is a fraction whose denominator is 100. In fact you can think of the phrase 'per cent' meaning 'out of 100'. We use the symbol % to represent a percentage, as earlier. The following three fractions all have a denominator of 100, and are expressed as percentages as shown:

$$\frac{17}{100} \quad \text{may be expressed as} \quad 17\%$$

$$\frac{50}{100} \quad \text{may be expressed as} \quad 50\%$$

$$\frac{3}{100} \quad \text{may be expressed as} \quad 3\%$$

WORKED EXAMPLE

4.1   Express $\frac{19}{100}$, $\frac{35}{100}$ and $\frac{17.5}{100}$ as percentages.

Solution   All of these fractions have a denominator of 100. So it is straightforward to write down their percentage form:

$$\frac{19}{100} = 19\% \quad \frac{35}{100} = 35\% \quad \frac{17.5}{100} = 17.5\%$$

Sometimes it is necessary to convert a fraction whose denominator is not 100, for example $\frac{2}{5}$, into a percentage. This could be done by expressing the fraction as an equivalent fraction with denominator 100, as was explained in Section 2.2 on page 16. However, with calculators readily available, the calculation can be done as follows.

We can use the calculator to divide the numerator of the fraction by the denominator. The answer is then multiplied by 100. The resulting number is the required percentage. So, to convert $\frac{2}{5}$ we perform the following key strokes:

$$2 \div 5 \times 100 = 40$$

and so $\frac{2}{5} = 40\%$. You should check this now using your own calculator,

Key point   To convert a fraction to a percentage, divide the numerator by the denominator, multiply by 100 and then label the result as a percentage.

WORKED EXAMPLES

4.2   Convert $\frac{5}{8}$ into a percentage.

Solution   Using the method described above we find

$$5 \div 8 \times 100 = 62.5$$

Labelling the answer as a percentage, we see that $\frac{5}{8}$ is equivalent to 62.5%.

4.3   Bill scores $\frac{13}{17}$ in a test. In a different test, Mary scores $\frac{14}{19}$. Express the scores as percentages, and thereby make a comparison of the two marks.

Solution   Use your calculator to perform the division and then multiply the result by 100.

Bill's score: $13 \div 17 \times 100 = 76.5$ (1 d.p.)

Mary's score: $14 \div 19 \times 100 = 73.7$ (1 d.p.)

So we see that Bill scores 76.5% and Mary scores 73.7%. Notice that in these percentage forms it is easy to compare the two marks. We see that Bill has achieved the higher score. Making easy comparisons like this is one of the reasons why percentages are used so frequently.

We have seen that percentages are fractions with a denominator of 100, so that, for example, $\frac{19}{100} = 19\%$. Sometimes a fraction may be given not as a numerator divided by a denominator, but in its decimal form. For example, the decimal form of $\frac{19}{100}$ is 0.19. To convert a decimal fraction into a percentage we simply multiply by 100. So

$$0.19 = 0.19 \times 100\% = 19\%$$

Key point

To convert a decimal fraction to a percentage, multiply by 100 and then label the result as a percentage.

We may also want to reverse the process. Frequently in business calculations involving formulae for interest it is necessary to express a percentage in its decimal form. To convert a percentage to its equivalent decimal form we divide the percentage by 100.

WORKED EXAMPLE

4.4   Express 50% as a decimal.

Solution   We divide the percentage by 100:

$$50 \div 100 = 0.5$$

So 50% is equivalent to 0.5. To see why this is the case, remember that 'per cent' literally means 'out of 100' so 50% means 50 out of 100, or $\frac{50}{100}$, or in its simplest form 0.5.

Key point

To convert a percentage to its equivalent decimal fraction form, divide by 100.

WORKED EXAMPLE

4.5   Express 17.5% as a decimal.

Solution   We divide the percentage by 100:

$$17.5 \div 100 = 0.175$$

So 17.5% is equivalent to 0.175.

Some percentages appear so frequently in everyday life that it is useful to learn their fraction and decimal fraction equivalent forms.

Key point

$$10\% = 0.1 = \tfrac{1}{10} \qquad 25\% = 0.25 = \tfrac{1}{4}$$

$$50\% = 0.5 = \tfrac{1}{2} \qquad 75\% = 0.75 = \tfrac{3}{4} \qquad 100\% = 1$$

Recall from §1.2 that 'of' means multiply.

We are often asked to calculate a percentage of a quantity: for example, find 17.5% of 160 or 10% of 95. Such calculations arise when finding discounts on prices. Since $17.5\% = \frac{17.5}{100}$ we find

$$17.5\% \text{ of } 160 = \frac{17.5}{100} \times 160 = 28$$

Because finding 10% of a quantity is equivalent to dividing by 10, it is easy to find 10% by moving the decimal point one place to the left.

and since $10\% = 0.1$ we may write

$$10\% \text{ of } 95 = 0.1 \times 95 = 9.5$$

WORKED EXAMPLES

4.6   Calculate 27% of 90.

Solution $$27\% \text{ of } 90 = \frac{27}{100} \times 90 = 24.3$$

4.7   Calculate 100% of 6.

Solution $$100\% \text{ of } 6 = \frac{100}{100} \times 6 = 6$$

Observe that 100% of a number is simply the number itself.

4.8   A deposit of £750 increases by 9%. Calculate the resulting deposit.

Solution   We first find 9% of 750. This is the amount by which the deposit has increased. Then

$$9\% \times 750 = \frac{9}{100} \times 750 = 67.50$$

The deposit has increased by £67.50. The resulting deposit is therefore $750 + 67.5 = £817.50$.

Alternatively we may perform the calculation as follows. The original deposit represents 100%. The deposit increases by 9% to 109% of the original. So the resulting deposit is 109% of £750:

$$109\% \times 750 = \frac{109}{100} \times 750 = 817.50$$

The resulting deposit is £817.50

4.9   A television set is advertised at £315. The retailer offers a 10% discount. How much do you pay for the television?

Solution $$10\% \text{ of } 315 = 31.50$$

The discount is £31.50 and so the cost is $315 - 31.5 = £283.50.$

Alternatively we can note that since the discount is 10%, then the selling price is 90% of the advertised price:

$$90\% \text{ of } 315 = \frac{90}{100} \times 315 = 283.50$$

Performing the calculation in the two ways will increase your understanding of percentages and serve as a check.

When a quantity changes, it is sometimes useful to calculate the **percentage change**. For example, suppose a worker earns £14,500 in the current year, and last year earned £13,650. The actual amount earned has changed by $14,500 - 13,650 = £850.$ The percentage change is calculated from the formula:

Key point

$$\text{percentage change} = \frac{\text{change}}{\text{original value}} \times 100 = \frac{\text{new value} - \text{original value}}{\text{original value}} \times 100$$

If the change is positive, then there has been an increase in the measured quantity. If the change is negative, then there has been a decrease in the quantity.

WORKED EXAMPLES

4.10   A worker's earnings increase from £13,650 to £14,500. Calculate the percentage change.

Solution

$$\text{percentage change} = \frac{\text{new value} - \text{original value}}{\text{original value}} \times 100$$

$$= \frac{14{,}500 - 13{,}650}{13{,}650} \times 100$$

$$= 6.23$$

The worker's earnings increased by 6.23%.

4.11   A microwave oven is reduced in price from £149.95 to £135. Calculate the percentage change in price.

Solution

$$\text{percentage change} = \frac{\text{new value} - \text{original value}}{\text{original value}} \times 100$$

$$= \frac{135 - 149.95}{149.95} \times 100$$

$$= -9.97$$

The negative result is indicative of the price decrease. The percentage change in price is approximately −10%.

Self-assessment question 4.1

1. Give one reason why it is sometimes useful to express fractions as percentages.

Exercise 4.1

1. Calculate 23% of 124.

2. Express the following as percentages:
    (a) $\dfrac{9}{11}$ (b) $\dfrac{15}{20}$ (c) $\dfrac{9}{10}$ (d) $\dfrac{45}{50}$ (e) $\dfrac{75}{90}$

3. Express $\frac{13}{12}$ as a percentage.

4. Calculate 217% of 500.

5. A worker earns £400 a week. She receives a 6% increase. Calculate her new weekly wage.

6. A debt of £1200 is decreased by 17%. Calculate the remaining debt.

7. Express the following percentages as decimals:
    (a) 50%   (b) 36%   (c) 75%
    (d) 100%   (e) 12.5%

8. A compact disc player normally priced at £256 is reduced in a sale by 20%. Calculate the sale price.

9. A bank deposit earns 7.5% interest in one year. Calculate the interest earned on a deposit of £15,000.

10. The cost of a car is increased from £6950 to £7495. Calculate the percentage change in price.

11. During a sale, a washing machine is reduced in price from £525 to £399. Calculate the percentage change in price.

4.2 Ratio

Ratios are simply an alternative way of expressing fractions. Consider the problem of dividing £200 between two people, Ann and Bill, in the ratio of 7 : 3. This means that Ann receives £7 for every £3 that Bill receives. So every £10 is divided as £7 to Ann and £3 to Bill. Thus Ann receives $\frac{7}{10}$ of the money. Now $\frac{7}{10}$ of £200 is $\frac{7}{10} \times 200 = 140$. So Ann receives £140 and Bill receives £60.

WORKED EXAMPLE

4.12   Divide 170 in the ratio 3 : 2.

Solution   A ratio of $3 : 2$ means that every 5 parts are split as 3 and 2. That is, the first number is $\frac{3}{5}$ of the total; the second number is $\frac{2}{5}$ of the total. So

$$\frac{3}{5} \text{ of } 170 = \frac{3}{5} \times 170 = 102$$

$$\frac{2}{5} \text{ of } 170 = \frac{2}{5} \times 170 = 68$$

The number is divided into 102 and 68.

Note from Worked Example 4.12 that to split a number in a given ratio we first find the total number of parts. The total number of parts is found by adding the numbers in the ratio. For example, if the ratio is given as *m:n*, the total number of parts is $m + n$. Then these $m + n$ parts are split into two with the first number being $\frac{m}{m + n}$ of the total, and the second number being $\frac{n}{m + n}$ of the total. Compare this with Worked Example 4.12.

WORKED EXAMPLE

4.13   Divide 250 cm in the ratio $1 : 3 : 4$.

Solution   Every 8 cm is divided into 1 cm, 3 cm and 4 cm. Thus the first length is $\frac{1}{8}$ of the total, the second length is $\frac{3}{8}$ of the total, and the third length is $\frac{4}{8}$ of the total:

$$\frac{1}{8} \text{ of } 250 = \frac{1}{8} \times 250 = 31.25$$

$$\frac{3}{8} \text{ of } 250 = \frac{3}{8} \times 250 = 93.75$$

$$\frac{4}{8} \text{ of } 250 = \frac{4}{8} \times 250 = 125$$

The 250 cm length is divided into 31.25 cm, 93.75 cm and 125 cm.

Ratios can be written in different ways. The ratio $3 : 2$ can also be written as $6 : 4$. This is clear if we note that $6 : 4$ is a total of 10 parts split as $\frac{6}{10}$ and $\frac{4}{10}$ of the total. Since $\frac{6}{10}$ is equivalent to $\frac{3}{5}$, and $\frac{4}{10}$ is equivalent to $\frac{2}{5}$, we see that $6 : 4$ is equivalent to $3 : 2$.

Generally, any ratio can be expressed as an equivalent ratio by multiplying or dividing each term in the ratio by the same number. So, for example,

5 : 3 is equivalent to 15 : 9

and

$\frac{3}{4}$: 2 is equivalent to 3 : 8

WORKED EXAMPLES

4.14   Divide a mass of 380 kg in the ratio $\frac{3}{4} : \frac{1}{5}$.

Solution   It is simpler to work with whole numbers, so first of all we produce an equivalent ratio by multiplying each term, first by 4, and then by 5, to give

$$\frac{3}{4} : \frac{1}{5} = 3 : \frac{4}{5} = 15 : 4$$

Note that this is equivalent to multiplying through by the lowest common multiple of 4 and 5.

So dividing 380 kg in the ratio $\frac{3}{4} : \frac{1}{5}$ is equivalent to dividing it in the ratio 15 : 4.

Now the total number of parts is 19 and so we split the 380 kg mass as

$$\frac{15}{19} \times 380 = 300$$

and

$$\frac{4}{19} \times 380 = 80$$

The total mass is split into 300 kg and 80 kg.

4.15   Bell metal, which is a form of bronze, is used for casting bells. It is an alloy of copper and tin. To manufacture bell metal requires 17 parts of copper to every 3 parts of tin.

(a)   Express this requirement as a ratio.

(b)   Express the amount of tin required as a percentage of the total.

(c)   If the total amount of tin in a particular casting is 150 kg, find the amount of copper.

Solution   (a)   Copper and tin are needed in the ratio 17 : 3.

(b) $\frac{3}{20}$ of the alloy is tin. Since $\frac{3}{20} = 15\%$ we find that 15% of the alloy is tin.

(c) A mass of 150 kg of tin makes up 15% of the total. So 1% of the total would have a mass of 10 kg. Copper, which makes up 85%, will have a mass of 850 kg.

Self-assessment question 4.2

1. Dividing a number in the ratio 2 : 3 is the same as dividing it in the ratio 10 : 15. True or false?

Exercise 4.2

1. Divide 180 in the ratio 8 : 1 : 3.

2. Divide 930 cm in the ratio 1 : 1 : 3.

3. A 6 m length of wood is cut in the ratio 2 : 3 : 4. Calculate the length of each piece.

4. Divide 1200 in the ratio 1 : 2 : 3 : 4.

5. A sum of £2600 is divided between Alan, Bill and Claire in the ratio of $2\frac{3}{4} : 1\frac{1}{2} : 2\frac{1}{4}$. Calculate the amount that each receives.

6. A mass of 40 kg is divided into three portions in the ratio 3 : 4 : 8. Calculate the mass of each portion.

7. Express the following ratios in their simplest forms:
    (a) 12 : 24   (b) 3 : 6   (c) 3 : 6 : 12
    (d) $\frac{1}{3} : 7$

8. A box contains two sizes of nails. The ratio of long nails to short nails is 2 : 7. Calculate the number of each type if the total number of nails is 108.

Test and assignment exercises 4

1. Express as decimals
    (a) 8%   (b) 18%   (c) 65%

2. Express as percentages
    (a) $\frac{3}{8}$ (b) $\frac{79}{100}$ (c) $\frac{56}{118}$

3. Calculate 27.3% of 1496.

4. Calculate 125% of 125.

5. Calculate 85% of 0.25.

6. Divide 0.5 in the ratio 2 : 4 : 9.

7. A bill totals £234.5 to which is added tax at 17.5%. Calculate the amount of tax to be paid.

8. An inheritance is divided between three people in the ratio 4 : 7 : 2. If the least amount received is £2300 calculate how much the other two people received.

9. Divide 70 in the ratio of 0.5 : 1.3 : 2.1.

10. Divide 50% in the ratio 2 : 3.

11. The temperature of a liquid is reduced from 39 °C to 35 °C. Calculate the percentage change in temperature.

12. A jacket priced at £120 is reduced by 30% in a sale. Calculate the sale price of the jacket.

13. The price of a car is reduced from £7250 to £6450. Calculate the percentage change in price.

14. The population of a small town increases from 17296 to 19437 over a five-year period. Calculate the percentage change in population.

15. A number, X, is increased by 20% to form a new number Y. Y is then decreased by 20% to form a third number Z. Express Z in terms of X.

Algebra

5

Objectives: This chapter:

- explains what is meant by 'algebra'
- introduces important algebraic notations
- explains what is meant by a 'power' or 'index'
- illustrates how to evaluate an expression
- explains what is meant by a 'formula'

5.1 What is algebra?

In order to extend the techniques of arithmetic so that they can be more useful in applications we introduce letters or **symbols** to represent quantities of interest. For example, we may choose the capital letter I to stand for the *interest rate* in a business calculation, or the lower case letter t to stand for the *time* in a scientific calculation, and so on. The choice of which letter to use for which quantity is largely up to the user, although some conventions have been developed. Very often the letters x and y are used to stand for arbitrary quantities. **Algebra** is the body of mathematical knowledge that has been developed to manipulate symbols. Some symbols take fixed and unchanging values, and these are known as **constants.** For example, suppose we let the symbol b stand for the boiling point of water. This is fixed at 100 °C, and so b is a constant. Some symbols represent quantities that can vary, and these are called **variables.** For example, the velocity of a car might be represented by the symbol v, and might vary from 0 to 100 kilometres per hour.

Algebraic notation

In algebraic work, particular attention must be paid to the type of symbol used, so that, for example, the symbol T is quite different from the symbol t. Usually the symbols chosen are letters from the English alphabet although we frequently meet Greek letters. You may already be aware that the Greek letter 'pi', which

Table 5.1
The Greek alphabet

A	α	alpha	I	ι	iota	P	ρ	rho
B	β	beta	K	κ	kappa	Σ	σ	sigma
Γ	γ	gamma	Λ	λ	lambda	T	τ	tau
Δ	δ	delta	M	μ	mu	Y	υ	upsilon
E	ε	epsilon	N	ν	nu	Φ	ϕ	phi
Z	ζ	zeta	Ξ	ξ	xi	X	χ	chi
H	η	eta	O	o	omicron	Ψ	ψ	psi
Θ	θ	theta	Π	π	pi	Ω	ω	omega

Your scientific calculator is pre-programmed with the value of π. Check that you can use it.

has the symbol π, is used in the formula for the area of a circle, and is equal to the constant $3.14159\ldots$. In many calculations π can be approximated by $\frac{22}{7}$. For reference the full Greek alphabet is given in Table 5.1.

Another important feature is the position of a symbol in relation to other symbols. As we shall see in this chapter, the quantities xy, x^y, y^x and x_y all can mean quite different things. When a symbol is placed to the right and slightly higher than another symbol it is referred to as a **superscript.** So the quantity x^y contains the superscript y. Likewise, if a symbol is placed to the right and slightly lower than another symbol it is called a **subscript.** The quantity x_1 contains the subscript 1.

The arithmetic of symbols

Addition ($+$) If the letters x and y stand for two numbers, their **sum** is written as $x + y$. Note that $x + y$ is the same as $y + x$ just as $4 + 7$ is the same as $7 + 4$.

Subtraction ($-$) The quantity $x - y$ is called the **difference** of x and y, and means the number y subtracted from the number x. Note that $x - y$ is not the same as $y - x$, in the same way that $5 - 3$ is different from $3 - 5$.

Multiplication ($\times$) Five times the number x is written $5 \times x$, although when multiplying the $\times$ sign is sometimes replaced with '$\cdot$', or is even left out altogether. This means that $5 \times x$, $5 \cdot x$ and $5x$ all mean five times the number x. Similarly $x \times y$ can be written $x \cdot y$ or simply xy. When multiplying, the order of the symbols is not important, so that xy is the same as yx just as 5×4 is the same as 4×5. The quantity xy is also known as the **product** of x and y.

Division ($\div$) $x \div y$ means the number, or expression, x, divided by the number or expression y. This is usually written as $\frac{x}{y}$ or x/y. Here the order is important and $\frac{x}{y}$ is different from $\frac{y}{x}$. An expression involving one symbol divided by another is known as an **algebraic fraction.** The top line, that is, the x in $\frac{x}{y}$, is called the **numerator** and the bottom line, that is, the y, is called the **denominator.** The quantity $\frac{x}{y}$ is known as the **quotient** of x and y.

A quantity made up of symbols together with $+, -, \times$ or $\div$ is called an **algebraic expression.** When evaluating an algebraic expression the BODMAS rule given in Chapter 1 applies. This rule reminds us of the correct order in which to evaluate an expression.

Self-assessment questions 5.1

1. Explain what you understand by the term 'algebra'.

2. If m and n are two numbers, explain what is meant by mn.

3. What is an algebraic fraction? Explain the meaning of the terms 'numerator' and 'denominator'.

4. What is the distinction between a superscript and a subscript?

5. What is the distinction between a variable and a constant?

5.2   Powers or indices

Frequently we shall need to multiply a number by itself several times, for example $3 \times 3 \times 3$, or $a \times a \times a \times a$.

To abbreviate such quantities a new notation is introduced. $a \times a \times a$ is written a^3, pronounced 'a cubed'. The superscript 3 is called a **power** or **index** and the letter a is called the **base.** Similarly $a \times a$ is written a^2, pronounced 'a squared' or 'a raised to the power 2'.

Most calculators have a button marked x^y, which can be used to evaluate expressions such as 2^8, 3^{11} and so on. Check to see whether your calculator can do these by verifying that $2^8 = 256$ and $3^{11} = 177147$. Note that the plural of index is **indices.**

As a^2 means $a \times a$, and a^3 means $a \times a \times a$, then we interpret a^1 as simply a. That is, any number raised to the power 1 is itself.

The calculator button x^y is used to find powers of numbers.

Key point   Any number raised to the power 1 is itself, that is $a^1 = a$.

WORKED EXAMPLES

5.1   In the expression 3^8 identify the index and the base.

Solution   In the expression 3^8, the index is 8 and the base is 3.

5.2   Explain what is meant by y^5.

Solution y^5 means $y \times y \times y \times y \times y$.

5.3   Explain what is meant by $x^2 y^3$.

Solution x^2 means $x \times x$; y^3 means $y \times y \times y$. Therefore $x^2 y^3$ means $x \times x \times y \times y \times y$.

5.4   Evaluate 2^3 and 3^4.

Solution 2^3 means $2 \times 2 \times 2$, that is 8. Similarly 3^4 means $3 \times 3 \times 3 \times 3$, that is 81.

5.5   Explain what is meant by 7^1.

Solution   Any number to the power 1 is itself, that is 7^1 is simply 7.

5.6   Evaluate 10^2 and 10^3.

Solution 10^2 means 10×10 or 100. Similarly 10^3 means $10 \times 10 \times 10$ or 1000.

5.7   Use indices to write the expression $a \times a \times b \times b \times b$ more compactly.

Solution $a \times a$ can be written a^2; $b \times b \times b$ can be written b^3. Therefore $a \times a \times b \times b \times b$ can be written as $a^2 \times b^3$ or simply $a^2 b^3$.

5.8   Write out fully $z^3 y^2$.

Solution $z^3 y^2$ means $z \times z \times z \times y \times y$. Note that we could also write this as $zzzyy$.

We now consider how to simplify and evaluate expressions involving not only powers but other operations as well. Recall from Section 1.2 that the BODMAS rule tells us the order in which operations should be carried out, but the rule makes no reference to powers. In fact, powers should be given higher priority than the other operations ($\times$, $\div$, $+$, $-$) and evaluated first. Consider the expression -4^2. Because the power must be evaluated before the subtraction -4^2 is equal to -16. On the other hand, $(-4)^2$ means $(-4)(-4)$ which is equal to $+16$.

We now introduce the BIDMAS rule. This is a modification of the BODMAS rule introduced in Section 1.2. BIDMAS is used when evaluating or simplifying expressions that contain indices as well as the other operations of addition, subtraction, multiplication and division.

BIDMAS stands for:

Bracket ( )	First priority
Indices	Second priority
Division $\div$	Third priority
Multiplication $\times$	Third priority
Addition $+$	Fourth priority
Subtraction $-$	Fourth priority

Note that in BIDMAS there is no mention of the word 'of'. This is in contrast to the BODMAS rule. In BIDMAS, 'of' is subsumed into multiplication. For example $\frac{2}{3}$ of 18 is treated as $\frac{2}{3} \times 18$.

We illustrate BIDMAS with some examples.

WORKED EXAMPLES

5.9   Evaluate (a) $- 5^2$, (b) $(- 5)^2$.

Solution

Recall that when a negative number is multiplied by another negative number the result is positive.

(a) The power is evaluated first. Noting that $5^2 = 25$, we see that $- 5^2 = -25$.

(b) $(- 5)^2$ means $(-5) \times (-5) = +25$.

Note how the brackets can significantly change the meaning of an expression.

5.10   Explain the meanings of $-x^2$ and $(-x)^2$. Are these different?

Solution

In the expression $-x^2$ it is the quantity x that is squared, so that $-x^2 = -(x \times x)$. On the other hand $(-x)^2$ means $(-x) \times (-x)$, which equals $+x^2$. The two expressions are not the same.

5.11   Evaluate   (a) $(1 + 2^3)^2$ (b) $\frac{2^3 - 1}{2^2 + 3}$.

Solution

(a) The bracketed expression, $1 + 2^3$, is evaluated first. In this expression, the index term, 2^3, has priority and is evaluated first. So

$$1 + 2^3 = 1 + 8 = 9$$

Hence

$$(1 + 2^3)^2 = 9^2 = 81$$

(b) Although the fraction as presented does not contain any brackets, it is necessary to consider brackets around both the numerator and the denominator. So $\frac{2^3 - 1}{2^2 + 3}$ is treated as $\frac{(2^3 - 1)}{(2^2 + 3)}$.

The numerator and denominator are each evaluated separately. Using BIDMAS we evaluate the power terms first. Thus

$$2^3 - 1 = 8 - 1 = 7, \quad 2^2 + 3 = 4 + 3 = 7$$

The fraction can now be evaluated.

$$\frac{2^3 - 1}{2^2 + 3} = \frac{7}{7} = 1$$

5.12   Simplify $x^2y^2 + 3(xy)^2$.

Solution

The bracketed expression is simplified first.

$$(xy)^2 = (xy)(xy) = x^2y^2$$

So we have

$$x^2y^2 + 3(xy)^2 = x^2y^2 + 3x^2y^2$$

Now x^2y^2 and $3x^2y^2$ are "like terms" (see Section 7.1). These can be added to give $4x^2y^2$. Thus

$$x^2y^2 + 3(xy)^2 = 4x^2y^2$$

Following the previous examples we emphasise again the importance of the position of brackets in an expression.

Self-assessment questions 5.2

1. Explain the meaning of the terms 'power' and 'base'.

2. What is meant by an index?

3. Explain the distinction between $(xyz)^2$ and xyz^2.

4. Explain the distinction between $(-3)^4$ and -3^4.

Exercise 5.2

1. Evaluate the following without using a calculator: 2^4, $(\frac{1}{2})^2$, 1^8, 3^5 and 0^3.

2. Evaluate 10^4, 10^5 and 10^6 without using a calculator.

3. Use a calculator to evaluate 11^4, 16^8, 39^4 and 1.5^7.

4. Write out fully (a) a^4b^2c and (b) xy^2z^4.

5. Write the following expressions compactly using indices:
   (a) $xxxyyx$ (b) $xxyyzzz$
   (c) $xyzxyz$ (d) $abccba$

6. Using a calculator, evaluate
   (a) 7^4 (b) 7^5 (c) $7^4 \times 7^5$ (d) 7^9
   (e) 8^3 (f) 8^7 (g) $8^3 \times 8^7$ (h) 8^{10}

   Can you spot a rule for multiplying numbers with powers?

7. Without using a calculator, find $(-3)^3$, $(-2)^2$, $(-1)^7$ and $(-1)^4$.

8. Use a calculator to find $(-16.5)^3$, $(-18)^2$ and $(-0.5)^5$.

9. Without using a calculator find
   (a) $(-6)^2$ (b) $(-3)^2$ (c) $(-4)^3$
   (d) $(-2)^3$
   Carefully compare your answers with the results of finding -6^2, -3^2, -4^3 and -2^3.

10. Simplify the following
    (a) $(2x)^2 + (3x)^2 - 10x^2$
    (b) $(2x + 3x)^2 - 10x^2$
    (c) $(2x)^2 + (3x - 10x)^2$
    (d) $(2x + 3x - 10x)^2$
    (e) $[(2 + 3)x]^2 - 10x^2$

5.3 Substitution and formulae

Substitution means replacing letters by actual numerical values.

WORKED EXAMPLES

5.13   Find the value of a^4 when $a = 3$.

Solution a^4 means $a \times a \times a \times a$. When we **substitute** the number 3 in place of the letter a we find 3^4 or $3 \times 3 \times 3 \times 3$, that is 81.

5.14   Find the value of $a + 7b + 3c$ when $a = 1, b = 2$ and $c = 3$.

Solution   Letting $b = 2$ we note that $7b = 14$. Letting $c = 3$ we note that $3c = 9$. Therefore, with $a = 1$,

$$a + 7b + 3c = 1 + 14 + 9 = 24$$

5.15   If $x = 4$, find the value of (a) $8x^3$ and (b) $(8x)^3$.

Solution   (a) Substituting $x = 4$ into $8x^3$ we find $8 \times 4^3 = 8 \times 64 = 512$.

(b) Substituting $x = 4$ into $(8x)^3$ we obtain $(32)^3 = 32768$. Note that the use of brackets makes a significant difference to the result.

5.16   Evaluate mk, mn and nk when $m = 5$, $n = -4$ and $k = 3$.

Solution $mk = 5 \times 3 = 15$. Similarly $mn = 5 \times (-4) = -20$ and $nk = (-4) \times 3 = -12$.

5.17   Find the value of $-7x$ when (a) $x = 2$ and (b) $x = -2$.

Solution   (a) Substituting $x = 2$ into $-7x$ we find -7×2, which equals -14.

(b) Substituting $x = -2$ into $-7x$ we find -7×-2, which equals 14.

5.18   Find the value of x^2 when $x = -3$.

Solution   Because x^2 means $x \times x$, its value when $x = -3$ is -3×-3, that is $+9$.

5.19   Find the value of $-x^2$ when $x = -3$.

Solution   Recall that a power is evaluated first. So $-x^2$ means $-(x \times x)$. When $x = -3$, this evaluates to $-(-3 \times -3) = -9$.

5.20   Find the value of $x^2 + 3x$ when (a) $x = 2$, (b) $x = -2$.

Solution   (a) Letting $x = 2$ we find

$$x^2 + 3x = (2)^2 + 3(2) = 4 + 6 = 10$$

(b) Letting $x = -2$ we find

$$x^2 + 3x = (-2)^2 + 3(-2) = 4 - 6 = -2$$

5.21   Find the value of $\frac{3x^2}{4} + 5x$ when $x = 2$.

Solution   Letting $x = 2$ we find

$$\frac{3x^2}{4} + 5x = \frac{3(2)^2}{4} + 5(2)$$

$$= \frac{12}{4} + 10$$

$$= 13$$

5.22   Find the value of $\frac{x^3}{4}$ when $x = 0.5$.

Solution   When $x = 0.5$ we find

$$\frac{x^3}{4} = \frac{0.5^3}{4} = 0.03125$$

A **formula** is used to relate two or more quantities. You may already be familiar with the common formula used to find the area of a rectangle:

area = length × breadth

In symbols, writing A for area, l for length and b for breadth we have

$A = l \times b$ or simply $A = lb$

If we are now given particular numerical values for l and b we can use this formula to find A.

WORKED EXAMPLES

5.23   Use the formula $A = lb$ to find A when $l = 10$ and $b = 2.5$.

Solution   Substituting the values $l = 10$ and $b = 2.5$ into the formula $A = lb$ we find $A = 10 \times 2.5 = 25$.

5.24   The formula $V = IR$ is used by electrical engineers. Find the value of V when $I = 12$ and $R = 7$.

Solution   Substituting $I = 12$ and $R = 7$ in $V = IR$ we find $V = 12 \times 7 = 84$.

5.25   Use the formula $y = x^2 + 3x + 4$ to find y when $x = -2$.

Solution   Substituting $x = -2$ into the formula gives

$$y = (-2)^2 + 3(-2) + 4 = 4 - 6 + 4 = 2$$

Self-assessment questions 5.3

1. What is the distinction between an algebraic expression and a formula?

Exercise 5.3

1. Evaluate $3x^2y$ when $x = 2$ and $y = 5$.

2. Evaluate $8x + 17y - 2z$ when $x = 6$, $y = 1$ and $z = -2$.

3. The area A of a circle is found from the formula $A = \pi r^2$, where r is the length of the radius. Taking π to be 3.142 find the areas of the circles whose radii, in centimetres, are (a) $r = 10$, (b) $r = 3$, (c) $r = 0.2$.

4. Evaluate $3x^2$ and $(3x)^2$ when $x = 4$.

5. Evaluate $5x^2$ and $(5x)^2$ when $x = -2$.

6. If $y = 4.85$, find
    (a) $7y$ (b) y^2 (c) $5y + 2.5$
    (d) $y^3 - y$

7. If $a = 12.8$, $b = 3.6$ and $c = 9.1$, find
    (a) $a + b + c$ (b) ab (c) bc
    (d) abc

8. If $C = \frac{5}{9}(F - 32)$, find C when $F = 100$.

9. Evaluate (a) x^2, (b) $-x^2$ and (c) $(-x)^2$, when $x = 7$.

10. Evaluate the following when $x = -2$:
    (a) x^2 (b) $(-x)^2$ (c) $-x^2$
    (d) $3x^2$ (e) $-3x^2$ (f) $(-3x)^2$

11. Evaluate the following when $x = -3$:
    (a) $\frac{x^2}{3}$ (b) $(-x)^2$ (c) $-\left(\frac{x}{3}\right)^2$
    (d) $4x^2$ (e) $-4x^2$ (f) $(-4x)^2$

12. Evaluate $x^2 - 7x + 2$ when $x = -9$.

13. Evaluate $2x^2 + 3x - 11$ when $x = -3$.

14. Evaluate $-x^2 + 3x - 5$ when $x = -1$.

15. Evaluate $-9x^2 + 2x$ when $x = 0$.

16. Evaluate $5x^2 + x + 1$ when (a) $x = 3$, (b) $x = -3$, (c) $x = 0$, (d) $x = -1$.

17. Evaluate $\frac{2x^2}{3} - \frac{x}{2}$ when
    (a) $x = 6$ (b) $x = -6$ (c) $x = 0$
    (d) $x = 1$

18. Evaluate $\frac{4x^2}{5} + 3$ when
    (a) $x = 0$ (b) $x = 1$ (c) $x = 5$
    (d) $x = -5$

19. Evaluate $\frac{x^3}{2}$ when
    (a) $x = -1$ (b) $x = 2$ (c) $x = 4$

20. Use the formula $y = \frac{x^3}{2} + 3x^2$ to find y when
    (a) $x = 0$ (b) $x = 2$ (c) $x = 3$
    (d) $x = -1$

21. If $g = 2t^2 - 1$, find g when
    (a) $t = 3$ (b) $t = 0.5$ (c) $t = -2$

22. In business calculations, the simple interest earned on an investment, I, is calculated from the formula $I = Prn$, where P is the amount invested, r is the interest rate and n is the number of time periods. Evaluate I when
    (a) $P = 15000$, $r = 0.08$ and $n = 5$
    (b) $P = 12500$, $r = 0.075$ and $n = 3$.

23. An investment earning 'compound interest' has a value, S, given by $S = P(1 + r)^n$, where P is the amount invested, r is the interest rate and n is the number of time periods. Calculate S when
    (a) $P = 8250$, $r = 0.05$ and $n = 15$
    (b) $P = 125000$, $r = 0.075$ and $n = 11$.

VIDEO

Test and assignment exercises 5

1. Using a calculator, evaluate 44^3, 0.44^2 and 32.5^3.

2. Write the following compactly using indices:

   (a) $xxxyyyyy$ (b) $\dfrac{xxx}{yyyy}$ (c) a^2baab

3. Evaluate the expression $4x^3 yz^2$ when $x = 2$, $y = 5$ and $z = 3$.

4. The circumference C of a circle that has a radius of length r is given by the formula $C = 2\pi r$. Find the circumference of the circle with radius 0.5 cm. Take $\pi = 3.142$.

5. Find (a) $21^2 - 16^2$, (b) $(21 - 16)^2$. Comment upon the result.

6. If $x = 4$ and $y = -3$, evaluate

   (a) xy (b) $\dfrac{x}{y}$ (c) $\dfrac{x^2}{y^2}$ (d) $\left(\dfrac{x}{y}\right)^2$

7. Evaluate $2x(x + 4)$ when $x = 7$.

8. Evaluate $4x^2 + 7x$ when $x = 9$.

9. Evaluate $3x^2 - 7x + 12$ when $x = -2$.

10. Evaluate $-x^2 - 11x + 1$ when $x = -3$.

11. The formula $I = V/R$ is used by engineers. Find I when $V = 10$ and $R = 0.01$.

12. Given the formula $A = 1/x$, find A when (a) $x = 1$, (b) $x = 2$, (c) $x = 3$.

13. From the formula $y = 1/(x^2 + x)$ find y when (a) $x = 1$, (b) $x = -1$, (c) $x = 3$.

14. Find the value of $(-1)^n$ (a) when n is an even natural number and (b) when n is an odd natural number. (A natural number is a positive whole number.)

15. Find the value of $(-1)^{n+1}$ (a) when n is an even natural number and (b) when n is an odd natural number.

16. Evaluate
    (a) $2^2 + 3$,   (b) $(2 + 3)^2$,   (c) $(2^2 + 3)^2$ (d) 2×3^2 (e) $4 - 2 \times 3^2$

17. Simplify the following:-
    (a) $(2t)^2 - 2t^2$ (b) $[9r^2 - (3r)^2 + 1]^2$ (c) $x^2[3^2 - 2^3]^2$

Indices

Objectives: This chapter:

- states three laws used for manipulating indices
- shows how expressions involving indices can be simplified using the three laws
- explains the use of negative powers
- explains square roots, cube roots and fractional powers
- revises multiplication and division by powers of 10
- explains 'scientific notation' for representing very large and very small numbers

6.1 The laws of indices

Recall from Chapter 5 that an index is simply a power and that the plural of index is indices. Expressions involving indices can often be simplified if use is made of the **laws of indices**.

The first law

$$a^m \times a^n = a^{m+n}$$

In words, this states that if two numbers involving the same base but possibly different indices are to be multiplied together, their indices are added. Note that this law can be applied only if both bases are the same.

Key point   The first law: $a^m \times a^n = a^{m+n}$.

6.1   Use the first law of indices to simplify $a^4 \times a^3$.

Solution   Using the first law we have $a^4 \times a^3 = a^{4+3} = a^7$. Note that the same result could be obtained by actually writing out all the terms:

$$a^4 \times a^3 = (a \times a \times a \times a) \times (a \times a \times a) = a^7$$

6.2   Use the first law of indices to simplify $3^4 \times 3^5$.

Solution   From the first law $3^4 \times 3^5 = 3^{4+5} = 3^9$.

6.3   Simplify $a^4 a^7 b^2 b^4$.

Solution $a^4 a^7 b^2 b^4 = a^{4+7} b^{2+4} = a^{11} b^6$. Note that only those quantities with the same base can be combined using the first law.

The second law

$$\frac{a^m}{a^n} = a^{m-n}$$

In words, this states that if two numbers involving the same base but possibly different indices are to be divided, their indices are subtracted.

Key point
> The second law: $\dfrac{a^m}{a^n} = a^{m-n}$.

6.4   Use the second law of indices to simplify $\frac{a^5}{a^3}$.

Solution   The second law states that we subtract the indices, that is

$$\frac{a^5}{a^3} = a^{5-3} = a^2$$

6.5   Use the second law of indices to simplify $\frac{3^7}{3^4}$.

Solution   From the second law, $\frac{3^7}{3^4} = 3^{7-4} = 3^3$.

6.6   Using the second law of indices, simplify $\frac{x^3}{x^3}$.

Solution   Using the second law of indices we have $\frac{x^3}{x^3} = x^{3-3} = x^0$. However, note that any expression divided by itself equals 1, and so $\frac{x^3}{x^3}$ must equal 1. We can conclude from this that any number raised to the power 0 equals 1.

Key point
> Any number raised to the power 0 equals 1, that is $a^0 = 1$.

WORKED EXAMPLE

6.7   Evaluate (a) 14^0, (b) 0.5^0.

Solution   (a) Any number to the power 0 equals 1 and so $14^0 = 1$.

(b) Similarly, $0.5^0 = 1$.

The third law

$$(a^m)^n = a^{mn}$$

If a number is raised to a power, and the result is itself raised to a power, then the two powers are multiplied together.

Key point   The third law: $(a^m)^n = a^{mn}$.

WORKED EXAMPLES

6.8   Simplify $(3^2)^4$.

Solution   The third law states that the two powers are multiplied:

$$(3^2)^4 = 3^{2 \times 4} = 3^8$$

6.9   Simplify $(x^4)^3$.

Solution   Using the third law:

$$(x^4)^3 = x^{4 \times 3} = x^{12}$$

6.10   Remove the brackets from the expression $(2a^2)^3$.

Solution $(2a^2)^3$ means $(2a^2) \times (2a^2) \times (2a^2)$. We can write this as

$$2 \times 2 \times 2 \times a^2 \times a^2 \times a^2$$

or simply $8a^6$. We could obtain the same result by noting that both terms in the brackets, that is the 2 and the a^2, must be raised to the power 3, that is

$$(2a^2)^3 = 2^3(a^2)^3 = 8a^6$$

The result of the previous example can be generalised to any term of the form $(a^m b^n)^k$. To simplify such an expression we make use of the formula $(a^m b^n)^k = a^{mk} b^{nk}$.

Key point $(a^m b^n)^k = a^{mk} b^{nk}$

> **WORKED EXAMPLE**

6.11 Remove the brackets from the expression $(x^2y^3)^4$.

Solution Using the previous result we find

$$(x^2y^3)^4 = x^8y^{12}$$

We often need to use several laws of indices in one example.

> **WORKED EXAMPLES**

6.12 Simplify $\frac{(x^3)^4}{x^2}$.

Solution $(x^3)^4 = x^{12}$ using the third law of indices

So

$$\frac{(x^3)^4}{x^2} = \frac{x^{12}}{x^2} = x^{10}$$ using the second law

6.13 Simplify $(t^4)^2(t^2)^3$.

Solution $(t^4)^2 = t^8,$ $(t^2)^3 = t^6$ using the third law

So

$$(t^4)^2(t^2)^3 = t^8 t^6 = t^{14}$$ using the first law

Self-assessment questions 6.1

1. State the three laws of indices.
2. Explain what is meant by a^0.
3. Explain what is meant by x^1.

Exercise 6.1

1. Simplify
   (a) $5^7 \times 5^{13}$ (b) $9^8 \times 9^5$
   (c) $11^2 \times 11^3 \times 11^4$

2. Simplify
   (a) $\dfrac{15^3}{15^2}$ (b) $\dfrac{4^{18}}{4^9}$ (c) $\dfrac{5^{20}}{5^{19}}$

3. Simplify
   (a) $a^7 a^3$ (b) $a^4 a^5$ (c) $b^{11} b^{10} b$

4. Simplify
   (a) $x^7 \times x^8$ (b) $y^4 \times y^8 \times y^9$

5. Explain why the laws of indices cannot be used to simplify $19^8 \times 17^8$.

6. Simplify
   (a) $(7^3)^2$ (b) $(4^2)^8$ (c) $(7^9)^2$

7. Simplify $\dfrac{1}{(5^3)^8}$.

8. Simplify
   (a) $(x^2 y^3)(x^3 y^2)$ (b) $(a^2 b c^2)(b^2 c a)$

VIDEO

9. Remove the brackets from
   (a) $(x^2 y^4)^5$ (b) $(9x^3)^2$ (c) $(-3x)^3$
   (d) $(-x^2 y^3)^4$

10. Simplify
   (a) $\dfrac{(z^2)^3}{z^3}$ (b) $\dfrac{(y^3)^2}{(y^2)^2}$ (c) $\dfrac{(x^3)^2}{(x^2)^3}$

VIDEO

6.2 Negative powers

Sometimes a number is raised to a negative power. This is interpreted as follows:

$$a^{-m} = \frac{1}{a^m}$$

This can also be rearranged and expressed in the form

$$a^m = \frac{1}{a^{-m}}$$

Key point

$$a^{-m} = \frac{1}{a^m}, \qquad a^m = \frac{1}{a^{-m}}$$

For example,

$$3^{-2} \text{ means } \frac{1}{3^2}, \text{ that is } \frac{1}{9}$$

Similarly,

the number $\dfrac{1}{5^{-2}}$ can be written 5^2, or simply 25

To see the justification for this, note that because any number raised to the power 0 equals 1 we can write

$$\frac{1}{a^m} = \frac{a^0}{a^m}$$

Using the second law of indices to simplify the right-hand side we obtain $\frac{a^0}{a^m} = a^{0-m} = a^{-m}$ so that $\frac{1}{a^m}$ is the same as a^{-m}.

WORKED EXAMPLES

6.14   Evaluate

(a) 2^{-5} (b) $\dfrac{1}{3^{-4}}$

Solution   (a) $2^{-5} = \dfrac{1}{2^5} = \dfrac{1}{32}$ (b) $\dfrac{1}{3^{-4}} = 3^4$ or simply 81

6.15   Evaluate

(a) 10^{-1} (b) 10^{-2}

Solution   (a) 10^{-1} means $\frac{1}{10^1}$, or simply $\frac{1}{10}$. It is important to recognise that 10^{-1} is therefore the same as 0.1.

(b) 10^{-2} means $\frac{1}{10^2}$ or $\frac{1}{100}$. So 10^{-2} is therefore the same as 0.01.

6.16   Rewrite each of the following expressions using only positive powers:

(a) 7^{-3} (b) x^{-5}

Solution   (a) 7^{-3} means the same as $\frac{1}{7^3}$. The expression has now been written using a positive power.

(b) $x^{-5} = \frac{1}{x^5}$.

6.17   Rewrite each of the following expressions using only positive powers:

(a) $\dfrac{1}{x^{-9}}$ (b) $\dfrac{1}{a^{-4}}$

Solution   (a) $\dfrac{1}{x^{-9}} = x^9$ (b) $\dfrac{1}{a^{-4}} = a^4$

6.18   Rewrite each of the following using only negative powers:

(a) 6^8 (b) x^5 (c) z^a (d) $\dfrac{1}{b}$

Solution   (a) $6^8 = \dfrac{1}{6^{-8}}$ (b) $x^5 = \dfrac{1}{x^{-5}}$ (c) $z^a = \dfrac{1}{z^{-a}}$ (d) $\dfrac{1}{b} = b^{-1}$

6.19   Simplify

(a) $x^{-2}x^7$ (b) $\dfrac{x^{-3}}{x^{-5}}$

Solution   (a) To simplify $x^{-2}x^7$ we can use the first law of indices to write it as $x^{-2+7} = x^5$.

(b) To simplify $\dfrac{x^{-3}}{x^{-5}}$ we can use the second law of indices to write it as $x^{-3-(-5)} = x^{-3+5} = x^2$.

6.20   Simplify

(a) $(x^{-3})^5$ (b) $\dfrac{1}{(x^{-2})^2}$

Solution   (a) To simplify $(x^{-3})^5$ we can use the third law of indices and write it as $x^{-3\times5} = x^{-15}$. The answer could also be written as $\frac{1}{x^{15}}$.

(b) Note that $(x^{-2})^2 = x^{-4}$ using the third law. So $\dfrac{1}{(x^{-2})^2} = \dfrac{1}{x^{-4}}$. This could also be written as x^4.

6.21   Show that

$$\left(\frac{a}{b}\right)^{-1} = \frac{b}{a}$$

Solution   We know that

$$z^{-1} = \frac{1}{z^1} = \frac{1}{z}$$

Let $z = a/b$. Then

$$z^{-1} = \left(\frac{a}{b}\right)^{-1} = \frac{1}{a/b} = \frac{b}{a}$$

Self-assessment question 6.2

1. Explain how the negative power in a^{-m} is interpreted.

Exercise 6.2

1. Without using a calculator express each of the following as a proper fraction:
   (a) 2^{-2} (b) 2^{-3} (c) 3^{-2} (d) 3^{-3}
   (e) 5^{-2} (f) 4^{-2} (g) 9^{-1} (h) 11^{-2}
   (i) 7^{-1}

2. Express each of the following as decimal fractions:
   (a) 10^{-1} (b) 10^{-2} (c) 10^{-6} (d) $\frac{1}{10^2}$
   (e) $\frac{1}{10^3}$ (f) $\frac{1}{10^4}$

3. Write each of the following using only a positive power:
   (a) x^{-4} (b) $\frac{1}{x^{-5}}$ (c) x^{-7} (d) y^{-2}
   (e) $\frac{1}{y^{-1}}$ (f) y^{-1} (g) y^{-2} (h) z^{-1} (i) $\frac{1}{z^{-1}}$

4. Simplify the following using the laws of indices and write your results using only positive powers:
   VIDEO
   (a) $x^{-2}x^{-1}$ (b) $x^{-3}x^{-2}$ (c) x^3x^{-4}
   (d) $x^{-4}x^9$ (e) $\frac{x^{-2}}{x^{11}}$ (f) $(x^{-4})^2$
   (g) $(x^{-3})^3$ (h) $(x^2)^{-2}$

5. Simplify
   (a) $a^{13}a^{-2}$ (b) $x^{-9}x^{-7}$ (c) $x^{-21}x^2x$ (d) $(4^{-3})^2$

6. Evaluate
   (a) 10^{-3} (b) 10^{-4} (c) 10^{-5}

7. Evaluate $4^{-8}/4^{-6}$ and $3^{-5}/3^{-8}$ without using a calculator.

6.3 Square roots, cube roots and fractional powers

Square roots

Consider the relationship between the numbers 5 and 25. We know that $5^2 = 25$ and so 25 is the square of 5. Equivalently we say that 5 is a **square root** of 25. The symbol $\sqrt[2]{}$, or simply $\sqrt{}$, is used to denote a square root and we write

$$5 = \sqrt{25}$$

We can picture this as follows:

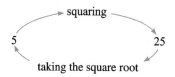

From this we see that taking the square root can be thought of as reversing the process of squaring.

We also note that

$$(-5) \times (-5) = (-5)^2$$
$$= 25$$

and so -5 is also a square root of 25. Hence we can write

$$-5 = \sqrt{25}$$

We can write both results together by using the 'plus or minus' sign $\pm$. We write

$$\sqrt{25} = \pm 5$$

In general, a **square root** of a number is a number that when squared gives the original number. Note that there are two square roots of any positive number. For a study of the square roots of negative numbers.

Most calculators enable you to find square roots although only the positive value is normally given. Look for a $\sqrt{}$ or 'sqrt' button on your calculator.

WORKED EXAMPLE

6.22 (a) Use your calculator to find $\sqrt{79}$ correct to 4 decimal places.

(b) Check your answers are correct by squaring them.

Solution (a) Using the $\sqrt{}$ button on the calculator you should verify that

$$\sqrt{79} = 8.8882 \text{ (to 4 decimal places)}$$

The second square root is -8.8882. Thus we can write

$$\sqrt{79} = \pm 8.8882$$

(b) Squaring either of the numbers ± 8.8882 we recover the original number, 79.

Cube roots

The **cube root** of a number is a number that when cubed gives the original number. The symbol for a cube root is $\sqrt[3]{}$. So, for example, since $2^3 = 8$ we can write $\sqrt[3]{8} = 2$.

We can picture this as follows:

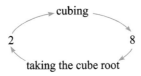

We can think of taking the cube root as reversing the process of cubing. As another example we note that $(-2)^3 = -8$ and hence $\sqrt[3]{-8} = -2$. All numbers, both positive and negative, possess a single, real cube root.

Your calculator may enable you to find a cube root. Look for a button marked $\sqrt[3]{}$. If so, check that you can use it correctly by verifying that

$$\sqrt[3]{46} = 3.5830$$

Fourth, fifth and other roots are defined in a similar way. For example, since

$$8^5 = 32768$$

we can write

$$\sqrt[5]{32768} = 8$$

Fractional powers

Sometimes fractional powers are used. The following example helps us to interpret a fractional power.

WORKED EXAMPLE

6.23   Simplify

(a) $x^{\frac{1}{2}}x^{\frac{1}{2}}$ (b) $x^{\frac{1}{3}}x^{\frac{1}{3}}x^{\frac{1}{3}}$

Use your results to interpret the fractional powers $\frac{1}{2}$ and $\frac{1}{3}$.

Solution   (a) Using the first law we can write

$$x^{\frac{1}{2}}x^{\frac{1}{2}} = x^{\frac{1}{2}+\frac{1}{2}} = x^1 = x$$

(b) Similarly,

$$x^{\frac{1}{3}}x^{\frac{1}{3}}x^{\frac{1}{3}} = x^{\frac{1}{3}+\frac{1}{3}+\frac{1}{3}} = x^1 = x$$

From (a) we see that

$$(x^{\frac{1}{2}})^2 = x$$

So when $x^{\frac{1}{2}}$ is squared, the result is x. Thus $x^{\frac{1}{2}}$ is simply the square root of x, that is

$$x^{\frac{1}{2}} = \sqrt{x}$$

Similarly, from (b)

$$(x^{\frac{1}{3}})^3 = x$$

and so $x^{\frac{1}{3}}$ is the cube root of x, that is

$$x^{\frac{1}{3}} = \sqrt[3]{x}$$

Key point

$$x^{\frac{1}{2}} = \sqrt{x}, \qquad x^{\frac{1}{3}} = \sqrt[3]{x}$$

More generally we have the following result:

Key point

$$x^{\frac{1}{n}} = \sqrt[n]{x}$$

Your scientific calculator will probably be able to find fractional powers. The button may be marked $x^{1/y}$ or $\sqrt[y]{x}$. Check that you can use it correctly by working through the following examples.

WORKED EXAMPLES

6.24   Evaluate to 3 decimal places, using a calculator:

(a) $3^{\frac{1}{4}}$ (b) $15^{1/5}$

Solution   Use your calculator to obtain the following solutions:

(a) 1.316   (b) 1.719

Note in part (a) that although the calculator gives just a single fourth root, there is another, -1.316.

6.25   Evaluate $(81)^{1/2}$.

Solution $(81)^{1/2} = \sqrt{81} = \pm 9$.

6.26   Explain what is meant by the number $27^{1/3}$.

Solution $27^{1/3}$ can be written $\sqrt[3]{27}$, that is the cube root of 27. The cube root of 27 is 3, since $3 \times 3 \times 3 = 27$, and so $27^{1/3} = 3$. Note also that since $27 = 3^3$ we can write

$$(27)^{1/3} = (3^3)^{1/3} = 3^{(3 \times 1/3)} \quad \text{using the third law}$$
$$= 3^1 \quad = 3$$

The following worked example shows how we deal with negative fractional powers.

6.27   Explain what is meant by the number $(81)^{-1/2}$.

Solution   Recall from our work on negative powers that $a^{-m} = 1/a^m$. Therefore we can write $(81)^{-1/2}$ as $1/(81)^{1/2}$. Now $81^{1/2} = \sqrt{81} = \pm 9$ and so

$$(81)^{-1/2} = \frac{1}{\pm 9} = \pm\frac{1}{9}$$

6.28   Write each of the following using a single index:

(a) $(5^2)^{\frac{1}{3}}$ (b) $(5^{-2})^{\frac{1}{3}}$

Solution   (a) Using the third law of indices we find

$$(5^2)^{\frac{1}{3}} = 5^{2\times\frac{1}{3}} = 5^{\frac{2}{3}}$$

Note that $(5^2)^{\frac{1}{3}}$ is the cube root of 5^2, that is $\sqrt[3]{25}$ or 2.9240.

(b) Using the third law of indices we find

$$(5^{-2})^{\frac{1}{3}} = 5^{-2\times\frac{1}{3}} = 5^{-\frac{2}{3}}$$

Note that there is a variety of equivalent ways in which this can be expressed, for example $\sqrt[3]{\frac{1}{5^2}}$ or $\sqrt[3]{\frac{1}{25}}$, or as $\frac{1}{5^{2/3}}$.

6.29   Write each of the following using a single index:

(a) $\sqrt{x^3}$ (b) $(\sqrt{x})^3$

Solution   (a) Because the square root of a number can be expressed as that number raised to the power $\frac{1}{2}$ we can write

$$\sqrt{x^3} = (x^3)^{\frac{1}{2}}$$

$$= x^{3\times\frac{1}{2}} \quad \text{using the third law}$$

$$= x^{\frac{3}{2}}$$

(b) $(\sqrt{x})^3 = (x^{\frac{1}{2}})^3$

$$= x^{\frac{3}{2}} \quad \text{using the third law}$$

Note from this example that $\sqrt{x^3} = (\sqrt{x})^3$.

Note that by generalising the results of the two previous worked examples we have the following:

Key point $a^{\frac{m}{n}} = \sqrt[n]{a^m} = (\sqrt[n]{a})^m$

6.30   Show that

(a) $\left(\dfrac{a}{b}\right)^{-\frac{m}{n}} = \left(\dfrac{b}{a}\right)^{\frac{m}{n}}$

(b) $\left(\dfrac{a}{b}\right)^{\frac{m}{n}} = \dfrac{a^{\frac{m}{n}}}{b^{\frac{m}{n}}}$

Solution   (a) $\left(\dfrac{a}{b}\right)^{-\frac{m}{n}} = \left[\left(\dfrac{a}{b}\right)^{-1}\right]^{\frac{m}{n}}$ using the third law of indices

$= \left(\dfrac{b}{a}\right)^{\frac{m}{n}}$ using Example 6.21

(b) $\left(\dfrac{a}{b}\right)^{\frac{m}{n}} = (ab^{-1})^{\frac{m}{n}}$

$= a^{\frac{m}{n}}(b^{-1})^{\frac{m}{n}}$ using the third law of indices

$= a^{\frac{m}{n}}b^{-\frac{m}{n}}$ using the third law of indices

$= \dfrac{a^{\frac{m}{n}}}{b^{\frac{m}{n}}}$ using the Key point in §6.2

Self-assessment questions 6.3

1. Explain the meaning of the fractional powers $x^{1/2}$ and $x^{1/3}$.
2. What are the square roots of 100?

Exercise 6.3

1. Evaluate
   (a) $64^{1/3}$ (b) $144^{1/2}$ (c) $16^{-1/4}$
   (d) $25^{-1/2}$ (e) $\dfrac{1}{32^{-1/5}}$

2. Simplify and then evaluate
   (a) $(3^{-1/2})^4$ (b) $(8^{1/3})^{-1}$

3. Write each of the following using a single index:
   (a) $\sqrt{8}$ (b) $\sqrt[3]{12}$ (c) $\sqrt[4]{16}$ (d) $\sqrt{13^3}$
   (e) $\sqrt[3]{4^7}$

4. Write each of the following using a single index:
   (a) $\sqrt{x}$ (b) $\sqrt[3]{y}$ (c) $\sqrt[2]{x^5}$ (d) $\sqrt[3]{5^7}$

6.4 Multiplication and division by powers of 10

To multiply and divide decimal fractions by powers of 10 is particularly simple. For example, to multiply 256.875 by 10 the decimal point is moved one place to the right, that is

$$256.875 \times 10 = 2568.75$$

To multiply by 100 the decimal point is moved two places to the right. So

$$256.875 \times 100 = 25687.5$$

To divide a number by 10, the decimal point is moved one place to the left. This is equivalent to multiplying by 10^{-1}. To divide by 100, the decimal point is moved two places to the left. This is equivalent to multiplying by 10^{-2}.

In general, to multiply a number by 10^n, the decimal point is moved n places to the right if n is a positive integer, and n places to the left if n is a negative integer. If necessary, additional zeros are inserted to make up the required number of digits. Consider the following example.

WORKED EXAMPLE

6.31   Without the use of a calculator, write down

(a) 75.45×10^3 (b) 0.056×10^{-2} (c) 96.3×10^{-3} (d) 0.00743×10^5

Solution   (a) The decimal point is moved three places to the right: $75.45 \times 10^3 = 75450$. It has been necessary to include an additional zero to make up the required number of digits.

(b) The decimal point is moved two places to the left: $0.056 \times 10^{-2} = 0.00056$.

(c) $96.3 \times 10^{-3} = 0.0963$.

(d) $0.00743 \times 10^5 = 743$.

Exercise 6.4

1. Without the use of a calculator write down:
   (a) 7.43×10^2 (b) 7.43×10^4 (c) 0.007×10^4 (d) 0.07×10^{-2}

2. Write each of the following as a multiple of 10^2:
   (a) 300   (b) 356   (c) 32   (d) 0.57

6.5 Scientific notation

It is often necessary to use very large numbers such as 65000000000 or very small numbers such as 0.000000001. **Scientific notation** can be used to express such numbers in a more concise form, which avoids writing very lengthy strings of numbers. Each number is written in the form

$$a \times 10^n$$

where a is usually a number between 1 and 10. We also make use of the fact that

$$10 = 10^1, \qquad 100 = 10^2, \qquad 1000 = 10^3 \text{ and so on}$$

and also that

$$10^{-1} = \frac{1}{10} = 0.1, \qquad 10^{-2} = \frac{1}{100} = 0.01 \text{ and so on}$$

Then, for example,

the number 4000 can be written $4 \times 1000 = 4 \times 10^3$

Similarly

the number 68000 can be written $6.8 \times 10000 = 6.8 \times 10^4$

and

the number 0.09 can be written $9 \times 0.01 = 9 \times 10^{-2}$

Note that all three numbers have been written in the form $a \times 10^n$ where a lies between 1 and 10.

WORKED EXAMPLES

6.32 Express the following numbers in scientific notation:

(a) 54   (b) -276 (c) 0.3

Solution (a) 54 can be written as 5.4×10, so in scientific notation we have 5.4×10^1.

(b) Negative numbers cause no problem: $-276 = -2.76 \times 10^2$.

(c) We can write 0.3 as 3×0.1 or 3×10^{-1}.

6.33 Write out fully the following numbers:

(a) 2.7×10^{-1} (b) 9.6×10^5 (c) -8.2×10^2

Solution (a) $2.7 \times 10^{-1} = 0.27$.

(b) $9.6 \times 10^5 = 9.6 \times 100000 = 960000$.

(c) $-8.2 \times 10^2 = -8.2 \times 100 = -820$.

6.34 Simplify the expression $(3 \times 10^2) \times (5 \times 10^3)$.

Solution The order in which the numbers are written down does not matter, and so we can write

$$(3 \times 10^2) \times (5 \times 10^3) = 3 \times 5 \times 10^2 \times 10^3 = 15 \times 10^5$$

Noting that $15 = 1.5 \times 10$ we can express the final answer in scientific notation:

$$15 \times 10^5 = 1.5 \times 10 \times 10^5 = 1.5 \times 10^6$$

Hence

$$(3 \times 10^2) \times (5 \times 10^3) = 1.5 \times 10^6$$

Self-assessment question 6.5

1. What is the purpose of using scientific notation?

Exercise 6.5

1. Express each of the following numbers in scientific notation:
   (a) 45   (b) 45000   (c) −450   (d) 90000000   (e) 0.15   (f) 0.00036   (g) 3.5
   (h) −13.2   (i) 1000000   (j) 0.0975   (k) 45.34

2. Write out fully the following numbers:
   (a) 3.75×10^2 (b) 3.97×10^1 (c) 1.875×10^{-1} (d) -8.75×10^{-3}

3. Simplify each of the following expressions, writing your final answer in scientific notation:
   (a) $(4 \times 10^3) \times (6 \times 10^4)$ (b) $(9.6 \times 10^4) \times (8.3 \times 10^3)$ (c) $(1.2 \times 10^{-3}) \times (8.7 \times 10^{-2})$
   (d) $\dfrac{9.37 \times 10^4}{6.14 \times 10^5}$ (e) $\dfrac{4.96 \times 10^{-2}}{9.37 \times 10^{-5}}$

Challenge Exercise 6

1. Simplify the following expressions:

   (a) $\sqrt{\left(\dfrac{27}{y^3}\right)^{-\frac{2}{3}}}$

   (b) $\left(\dfrac{48x^7y^{-1}}{3x^{-1}y^{-3}}\right)^{-\frac{3}{4}}$

   (c) $\sqrt{a\sqrt{\dfrac{b}{a}}\,\dfrac{c^2\sqrt{ab}}{b^{-1}c^{-2}}}$

Test and assignment exercises 6

1. Simplify

   (a) $\dfrac{z^5}{z^{-5}}$ (b) z^0 (c) $\dfrac{z^8 z^6}{z^{14}}$

2. Evaluate
   (a) $0.25^{1/2}$ (b) $(4096)^{1/3}$ (c) $(2601)^{1/2}$ (d) $16^{-1/2}$

3. Simplify $\dfrac{x^8 x^{-3}}{x^{-5} x^2}$.

4. Find the value of $(1/7)^0$.

5. Remove the brackets from

   (a) $(abc^2)^2$ (b) $(xy^2z^3)^2$ (c) $(8x^2)^{-3}$

6. Express each of the following numbers in scientific notation:

   (a) 5792   (b) 98.4   (c) 0.001   (d) -66.667

Simplifying algebraic expressions

7

Objectives: This chapter:

- describes a number of ways in which complicated algebraic expressions can be simplified

7.1 Addition and subtraction of like terms

Like terms are multiples of the same quantity. For example, $3y$, $72y$ and $0.5y$ are all multiples of y and so are like terms. Similarly, $5x^2$, $-3x^2$ and $\frac{1}{2}x^2$ are all multiples of x^2 and so are like terms. xy, $17xy$ and $-91xy$ are all multiples of xy and are therefore like terms. Like terms can be collected together and added or subtracted in order to simplify them.

WORKED EXAMPLES

7.1   Simplify $3x + 7x - 2x$.

Solution   All three terms are multiples of x and so are like terms. Therefore $3x + 7x - 2x = 8x$.

7.2   Simplify $3x + 2y$.

Solution $3x$ and $2y$ are not like terms. One is a multiple of x and the other is a multiple of y. The expression $3x + 2y$ cannot be simplified.

7.3   Simplify $x + 7x + x^2$.

Solution   The like terms are x and $7x$. These can be simplified to $8x$. Then $x + 7x + x^2 = 8x + x^2$. Note that $8x$ and x^2 are not like terms and so this expression cannot be simplified further.

7.4 Simplify $ab + a^2 - 7b^2 + 9ab + 8b^2$.

Solution The terms ab and $9ab$ are like terms. Similarly the terms $-7b^2$ and $8b^2$ are like terms. These can be collected together and then added or subtracted as appropriate. Thus

$$ab + a^2 - 7b^2 + 9ab + 8b^2 = ab + 9ab + a^2 - 7b^2 + 8b^2$$
$$= 10ab + a^2 + b^2$$

Exercise 7.1

1. Simplify, if possible,
    (a) $5p - 10p + 11q + 8q$ (b) $-7r - 13s + 2r + z$ (c) $181z + 13r - 2$
    (d) $x^2 + 3y^2 - 2y + 7x^2$ (e) $4x^2 - 3x + 2x + 9$

2. Simplify
    (a) $5y + 8p - 17y + 9q$ (b) $7x^2 - 11x^3 + 14x^2 + y^3$ (c) $4xy + 3xy + y^2$
    (d) $xy + yx$ (e) $xy - yx$

7.2 Multiplying algebraic expressions and removing brackets

Recall that when multiplying two numbers together the order in which we write them is irrelevant. For example, both 5×4 and 4×5 equal 20.

When multiplying three or more numbers together the order in which we carry out the multiplication is also irrelevant. By this we mean, for example, that when asked to multiply $3 \times 4 \times 5$ we can think of this as either $(3 \times 4) \times 5$ or as $3 \times (4 \times 5)$. Check for yourself that the result is the same, 60, either way.

It is also important to appreciate that $3 \times 4 \times 5$ could have been written as $(3)(4)(5)$.

It is essential that you grasp these simple facts about numbers in order to understand the algebra that follows. This is because identical rules are applied. Rules for determining the sign of the answer when multiplying positive and negative algebraic expressions are also the same as those used for multiplying numbers.

Key point

When multiplying

positive $\times$ positive $=$ positive
positive $\times$ negative $=$ negative
negative $\times$ positive $=$ negative
negative $\times$ negative $=$ positive

We introduce the processes involved in removing brackets using some simple examples.

WORKED EXAMPLES

7.5   Simplify $3(4x)$.

Solution   Just as with numbers $3(4x)$ could be written as $3 \times (4 \times x)$, and then as $(3 \times 4) \times x$, which evaluates to $12x$.
So $3(4x) = 12x$.

7.6   Simplify $5(3y)$.

Solution $5(3y) = 5 \times 3 \times y = 15y$.

7.7   Simplify $(5a)(3a)$.

Solution   Here we can write $(5a)(3a) = (5 \times a) \times (3 \times a)$. Neither the order in which we carry out the multiplications nor the order in which we write down the terms matters, and so we can write this as

$$(5a)(3a) = (5 \times 3)(a \times a)$$

As we have shown, it is usual to write numbers at the beginning of an expression. This simplifies to $15 \times a^2$, that is $15a^2$. Hence

$$(5a)(3a) = 15a^2$$

7.8   Simplify $4x^2 \times 7x^5$.

Solution   Recall that, when multiplying, the order in which we write down the terms does not matter. Therefore we can write

$$4x^2 \times 7x^5 = 4 \times 7 \times x^2 \times x^5$$

which equals $28x^{2+5} = 28x^7$.

7.9   Simplify $7(2b^2)$.

Solution $7(2b^2) = 7 \times (2 \times b^2) = (7 \times 2) \times b^2 = 14b^2$.

7.10   Simplify $(a) \times (-b)$

Solution   Here we have the product of a positive and a negative quantity. The result will be negative. We write

$$(a) \times (-b) = -ab$$

7.11   Explain the distinction between ab^2 and $(ab)^2$.

Solution ab^2 means $a \times b \times b$ whereas $(ab)^2$ means $(ab) \times (ab)$ which equals $a \times b \times a \times b$. The latter could also be written as a^2b^2.

7.12   Simplify (a) $(6z)(8z)$, (b) $(6z) + (8z)$, noting the distinction between the two results.

Solution   (a) $(6z)(8z) = 48z^2$.

(b) $(6z) + (8z)$ is the addition of like terms. This simplifies to $14z$.

7.13   Simplify (a) $(6x)(-2x)$, (b) $(-3y^2)(-2y)$.

Solution   (a) $(6x)(-2x)$ means $(6x) \times (-2x)$, which equals $-12x^2$.

(b) $(-3y^2)(-2y) = (-3y^2) \times (-2y) = 6y^3$.

Self-assessment questions 7.2

1. Two negative expressions are multiplied together. State the sign of the resulting product.

2. Three negative expressions are multiplied together. State the sign of the resulting product.

Exercise 7.2

1. Simplify each of the following:
    (a) $(4)(3)(7)$ (b) $(7)(4)(3)$ (c) $(3)(4)(7)$

2. Simplify
    (a) $5 \times (4 \times 2)$ (b) $(5 \times 4) \times 2$

3. Simplify each of the following:
    (a) $7(2z)$ (b) $15(2y)$ (c) $(2)(3)x$
    (d) $9(3a)$ (e) $(11)(5a)$ (f) $2(3x)$

4. Simplify each of the following:
    (a) $5(4x^2)$ (b) $3(2y^3)$ (c) $11(2u^2)$
    (d) $(2 \times 4) \times u^2$ (e) $(13)(2z^2)$

5. Simplify
    (a) $(7x)(3x)$ (b) $3a(7a)$ (c) $14a(a)$

6. Simplify
    (a) $5y(3y)$ (b) $5y + 3y$
    Explain why the two results are not the same.

7. Simplify each of the following:
    (a) $(abc)(a^2bc)$ (b) $x^2y(xy)$
    (c) $(xy^2)(xy^2)$

8. Explain the distinction, if any, between $(xy^2)(xy^2)$ and xy^2xy^2.

9. Explain the distinction, if any, between $(xy^2)(xy^2)$ and $(xy^2) + (xy^2)$. In both cases simplify the expressions.

10. Simplify
    (a) $(3z)(-7z)$ (b) $3z - 7z$

11. Simplify
    (a) $(-x)(3x)$ (b) $-x + 3x$

12. Simplify
    (a) $(-2x)(-x)$ (b) $-2x - x$

7.3 Removing brackets from $a(b + c)$, $a(b - c)$, $(a + b)(c + d)$ and $(a + b)(c - d)$

Recall from your study of arithmetic that the expression $(5 - 4) + 7$ is different from $5 - (4 + 7)$ because of the position of the brackets. In order to simplify an expression it is often necessary to remove brackets.

Removing brackets from expressions of the form $a(b + c)$ and $a(b - c)$

In an expression such as $a(b + c)$, it is intended that the a multiplies all the bracketed terms:

Key point — $a(b + c) = ab + ac$ Similarly: $a(b - c) = ab - ac$

WORKED EXAMPLES

7.14   Remove the brackets from

(a) $6(x + 5)$ (b) $8(2x - 4)$

Solution   (a) In the expression $6(x + 5)$ it is intended that the 6 multiplies both terms in the brackets. Therefore

$$6(x + 5) = 6x + 30$$

(b) In the expression $8(2x - 4)$ the 8 multiplies both terms in the brackets so that

$$8(2x - 4) = 16x - 32$$

7.15   Remove the brackets from the expression $7(5x + 3y)$.

Solution   The 7 multiplies both the terms in the brackets. Therefore

$$7(5x + 3y) = 7(5x) + 7(3y) = 35x + 21y$$

7.16   Remove the brackets from $-(x + y)$.

Solution   The expression $-(x + y)$ actually means $-1(x + y)$. It is intended that the -1 multiplies both terms in the brackets, therefore

$$-(x + y) = -1(x + y) = (-1) \times x + (-1) \times y = -x - y$$

7.17   Remove the brackets from the expression

$(x + y)z$

Solution   Note that the order in which we write down the terms to be multiplied does not matter, so that we can write $(x + y)z$ as $z(x + y)$. Then

$$z(x + y) = zx + zy$$

Alternatively, note that $(x + y)z = xz + yz$, which is an equivalent form of the answer.

7.18   Remove the brackets from the expressions

VIDEO

(a) $5(x - 2y)$ (b) $(x + 3)(-1)$

Solution   (a) $5(x - 2y) = 5x - 5(2y) = 5x - 10y$.

(b) $(x + 3)(-1) = (-1)(x + 3) = -1x - 3 = -x - 3$.

7.19 Simplify $x + 8(x - y)$.

Solution An expression such as this is simplified by first removing the brackets and then collecting together like terms. Removing the brackets we find

$$x + 8(x - y) = x + 8x - 8y$$

Collecting like terms we obtain $9x - 8y$.

7.20 Remove the brackets from

(a) $\frac{1}{2}(x + 2)$ (b) $\frac{1}{2}(x - 2)$ (c) $-\frac{1}{3}(a + b)$

Solution (a) In the expression $\frac{1}{2}(x + 2)$ it is intended that the $\frac{1}{2}$ multiplies both the terms in the brackets. So

$$\frac{1}{2}(x + 2) = \frac{1}{2}x + \frac{1}{2}(2) = \frac{1}{2}x + 1$$

(b) Similarly,

$$\frac{1}{2}(x - 2) = \frac{1}{2}x - \frac{1}{2}(2) = \frac{1}{2}x - 1$$

(c) In the expression $-\frac{1}{3}(a + b)$ the term $-\frac{1}{3}$ multiplies both terms in the brackets. So

$$-\frac{1}{3}(a + b) = -\frac{1}{3}a - \frac{1}{3}b$$

Removing brackets from expressions of the form $(a + b)(c + d)$ and $(a + b)(c - d)$

In the expression $(a + b)(c + d)$ it is intended that the quantity $(a + b)$ multiplies both the c and the d in the second brackets. Therefore

$$(a + b)(c + d) = (a + b)c + (a + b)d$$

Each of these two terms can be expanded further to give

$$(a + b)c = ac + bc \quad \text{and} \quad (a + b)d = ad + bd$$

Therefore

Key point $(a + b)(c + d) = ac + bc + ad + bd$

Similarly

$$(a + b)(c - d) = (a + b)c - (a + b)d$$

This can be expanded to give

$$(a + b)(c - d) = ac + bc - ad - bd$$

WORKED EXAMPLES

7.21   Remove the brackets from $(3 + x)(2 + y)$.

Solution $(3 + x)(2 + y) = (3 + x)(2) + (3 + x)y$

$$= 6 + 2x + 3y + xy$$

7.22   Remove the brackets from $(x + 6)(x - 3)$.

Solution $(x + 6)(x - 3) = (x + 6)x - (x + 6)3$

$$= x^2 + 6x - 3x - 18$$

$$= x^2 + 3x - 18$$

7.23   Remove the brackets from

(a) $(1 - x)(2 - x)$ (b) $(-x - 2)(2x - 1)$

Solution   (a) $(1 - x)(2 - x) = (1 - x)2 - (1 - x)x$

$$= 2 - 2x - x + x^2$$

$$= 2 - 3x + x^2$$

(b) $(-x - 2)(2x - 1) = (-x - 2)(2x) - (-x - 2)1$

$$= -2x^2 - 4x + x + 2$$

$$= -2x^2 - 3x + 2$$

7.24   Remove the brackets from the expression $3(x + 1)(x - 1)$.

VIDEO

Solution   First consider the expression $(x + 1)(x - 1)$:

$$(x + 1)(x - 1) = (x + 1)x - (x + 1)1$$

$$= x^2 + x - x - 1$$

$$= x^2 - 1$$

Then $3(x + 1)(x - 1) = 3(x^2 - 1) = 3x^2 - 3$.

Exercise 7.3

1. Remove the brackets from
   (a) $4(x + 1)$ (b) $-4(x + 1)$
   (c) $4(x - 1)$ (d) $-4(x - 1)$

2. Remove the brackets from
   (a) $5(x - y)$ (b) $19(x + 3y)$
   (c) $8(a + b)$ (d) $(5 + x)y$
   (e) $12(x + 4)$ (f) $17(x - 9)$
   (g) $-(a - 2b)$ (h) $\frac{1}{2}(2x + 1)$
   (i) $-3m(-2 + 4m + 3n)$

3. Remove the brackets and simplify the expressions:
   (a) $18 - 13(x + 2)$ (b) $x(x + y)$

4. Remove the brackets and simplify the following expressions:
   (a) $(x + 1)(x + 6)$ (b) $(x + 4)(x + 5)$
   (c) $(x - 2)(x + 3)$ (d) $(x + 6)(x - 1)$
   (e) $(x + y)(m + n)$ (f) $(4 + y)(3 + x)$
   (g) $(5 - x)(5 + x)$
   (h) $(17x + 2)(3x - 5)$

5. Remove the brackets and simplify the following expressions:
   (a) $(x + 3)(x - 7)$ (b) $(2x - 1)(3x + 7)$
   (c) $(4x + 1)(4x - 1)$
   (d) $(x + 3)(x - 3)$ (e) $(2 - x)(3 + 2x)$

6. Remove the brackets and simplify the following expressions:
   (a) $\frac{1}{2}(x + 2y) + \frac{7}{2}(4x - y)$

   (b) $\frac{3}{4}(x - 1) + \frac{1}{4}(2x + 8)$

7. Remove the brackets from
   (a) $-(x - y)$ (b) $-(a + 2b)$
   (c) $-\frac{1}{2}(3p + q)$

8. Remove the brackets from $(x + 1)(x + 2)$. Use your result to remove the brackets from $(x + 1)(x + 2)(x + 3)$.

Challenge Exercise 7

1. Remove the brackets and simplify the following expressions:
   (a) $(x^2 + 1)(x^2 - 1)$

   (b) $\left(\frac{1}{x} - 1\right)(x^2 - x)$

   (c) $(x^2 + x + 1)(x^2 - x - 1)$

Test and assignment exercises 7

1. Simplify
   (a) $7x^2 + 4x^2 + 9x - 8x$ (b) $y + 7 - 18y + 1$ (c) $a^2 + b^2 + a^3 - 3b^2$

2. Simplify
   (a) $(3a^2b) \times (-a^3b^2c)$ (b) $\frac{x^3}{-x^2}$

3. Remove the brackets from
   (a) $(a + 3b)(7a - 2b)$ (b) $x^2(x + 2y)$ (c) $x(x + y)(x - y)$

4. Remove the brackets from

   (a) $(7x + 2)(3x - 1)$ (b) $(1 - x)(x + 3)$ (c) $(5 + x)x$ (d) $(8x + 4)(7x - 2)$

5. Remove the brackets and simplify the following expressions:

   (a) $3x(x + 2) - 7x^2$ (b) $-(2a + 3b)(a + b)$ (c) $4(x + 7) + 13(x - 2)$

   (d) $5(2a + 5) - 3(5a - 2)$ (e) $\frac{1}{2}(a + 4b) + \frac{3}{2}a$

Functions

8

Objectives: This chapter:

- explains what is meant by a function
- describes the notation used to write functions
- explains the terms 'independent variable' and 'dependent variable'
- explains what is meant by a composite function
- explains what is meant by the inverse of a function

8.1 Definition of a function

A **function** is a rule that receives an input and produces an output. It is shown schematically in Figure 8.1. For example, the rule may be 'add 2 to the input'. If 6 is the input, then $6 + 2 = 8$ will be the output. If -5 is the input, then

Figure 8.1
A function produces an output from an input

$-5 + 2 = -3$ will be the output. In general, if x is the input then $x + 2$ will be the output. Figure 8.2 illustrates this function schematically.

Figure 8.2
The function adds 2 to the input

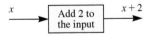

For a rule to be a function then it is crucial that only *one* output is produced for any given input.

Key point   A function is a rule that produces a *single* output for any given input.

The input to a function can usually take many values and so is called a **variable**. The output, too, varies depending upon the value of the input, and so is also a variable. The input is referred to as the **independent variable** because we are free to choose its value. The output is called the **dependent variable** because its value depends upon the value of the input.

8.2 Notation used for functions

We usually denote the input, the output and the function by letters or symbols. Commonly we use x to represent the input, y the output and f the function, although other letters will be used as well.

Consider again the example from §8.1. We let f be the function 'add 2 to the input' and we let x be the input. In mathematical notation we write

$$f : x \rightarrow x + 2$$

This means that the function f takes an input x and produces an output $x + 2$.

An alternative, but commonly used, notation is

$$f(x) = x + 2$$

The quantity $f(x)$ does not mean f times x but rather indicates that the function f acts on the quantity in the brackets. Because we also call the output y we can write $y = f(x) = x + 2$, or simply $y = x + 2$.

We could represent the same function using different letters. If h represents the function and t the input then we can write

$$h(t) = t + 2$$

WORKED EXAMPLES

8.1   A function multiplies the input by 4. Write down the function in mathematical notation.

Solution   Let us call the function f and the input x. Then we have

$$f : x \rightarrow 4x \quad \text{or alternatively} \quad f(x) = 4x$$

If we call the output y, we can write $y = f(x) = 4x$, or simply $y = 4x$.

8.2   A function divides the input by 6 and then adds 3 to the result. Write the function in mathematical notation.

Solution   Let us call the function z and the input t. Then we have

$$z(t) = \frac{t}{6} + 3$$

8.3   A function f is given by the rule $f: x \to 9$, or alternatively as $f(x) = 9$. Describe in words what this function does.

Solution   Whatever the value of the input to this function, the output is always 9.

8.4   A function squares the input and then multiplies the result by 6. Write down the function using mathematical notation.

Solution   Let us call the function f, the input x and the output y. Then

$$y = f(x) = 6x^2$$

8.5   Describe in words what the following functions do:

(a) $h(x) = \dfrac{1}{x}$ (b) $g(t) = t + t^2$

Solution   (a) The function $h(x) = \dfrac{1}{x}$ divides 1 by the input.

(b) The function $g(t) = t + t^2$ adds the input to the square of the input.

Often we are given a function and need to calculate the output from a given input.

WORKED EXAMPLES

8.6   A function f is defined by $f(x) = 3x + 1$. Calculate the output when the input is (a) 4, (b) -1, (c) 0.

Solution   The function f multiplies the input by 3 and then adds 1 to the result.

(a) When the input is 4, the output is $3 \times 4 + 1 = 12 + 1 = 13$. We write

$$f(x = 4) = 3(4) + 1 = 12 + 1 = 13$$

or more simply

$$f(4) = 13$$

Note that 4 has been substituted for x in the formula for f.

(b) We require the output when the input is -1, that is $f(-1)$:

$$f(x = -1) = f(-1) = 3(-1) + 1 = -3 + 1 = -2$$

The output is -2 when the input is -1.

(c) We require the output when the input is 0, that is $f(0)$:

$$f(x = 0) = f(0) = 3(0) + 1 = 0 + 1 = 1$$

8.7 A function g is defined by $g(t) = 2t^2 - 1$. Find

(a) $g(3)$ (b) $g(0.5)$ (c) $g(-2)$

Solution (a) We obtain $g(3)$ by substituting 3 for t:

$$g(3) = 2(3)^2 - 1 = 2(9) - 1 = 17$$

(b) $g(0.5) = 2(0.5)^2 - 1 = 0.5 - 1 = -0.5$.

(c) $g(-2) = 2(-2)^2 - 1 = 8 - 1 = 7$.

8.8 A function h is defined by $h(x) = \dfrac{x}{3} + 1$. Find

(a) $h(3)$ (b) $h(t)$ (c) $h(\alpha)$ (d) $h(2\alpha)$ (e) $h(2x)$

Solution (a) If $h(x) = \dfrac{x}{3} + 1$ then $h(3) = \dfrac{3}{3} + 1 = 1 + 1 = 2$.

(b) The function h divides the input by 3 and then adds 1. We require the output when the input is t, that is we require $h(t)$. Now

$$h(t) = \frac{t}{3} + 1$$

since the input t has been divided by 3 and then 1 has been added to the result. Note that $h(t)$ is obtained by substituting t in place of x in $h(x)$.

(c) We require the output when the input is α. This is obtained by substituting α in place of x. We find

$$h(\alpha) = \frac{\alpha}{3} + 1$$

(d) We require the output when the input is 2α. We substitute 2α in place of x. This gives

$$h(2\alpha) = \frac{2\alpha}{3} + 1$$

(e) We require the output when the input is $2x$. We substitute $2x$ in place of x. That is,

$$h(2x) = \frac{2x}{3} + 1$$

8.9 Given $f(x) = x^2 + x - 1$ write expressions for

(a) $f(\alpha)$ (b) $f(x + 1)$ (c) $f(2t)$

Solution (a) Substituting α in place of x we obtain

$$f(\alpha) = \alpha^2 + \alpha - 1$$

(b) Substituting $x + 1$ for x we obtain

$$f(x + 1) = (x + 1)^2 + (x + 1) - 1$$
$$= x^2 + 2x + 1 + x + 1 - 1$$
$$= x^2 + 3x + 1$$

(c) Substituting $2t$ in place of x we obtain

$$f(2t) = (2t)^2 + 2t - 1 = 4t^2 + 2t - 1$$

$<$ is the symbol for less than.
$\leqslant$ is the symbol for less than or equal to.
$\geqslant$ is the symbol for greater than or equal to.

Sometimes a function uses different rules on different intervals. For example, we could define a function as

$$f(x) = \begin{cases} 3x & \text{when} \quad 0 \leqslant x \leqslant 4 \\ 2x + 6 & \text{when} \quad 4 < x < 5 \\ 9 & \text{when} \quad x \geqslant 5 \end{cases}$$

Here the function is defined in three 'pieces'. The value of x determines which part of the definition is used to evaluate the function. The function is said to be a **piecewise** function.

WORKED EXAMPLE

8.10   A piecewise function is defined by

$$y(x) = \begin{cases} x^2 + 1 & \text{when} \quad -1 \leqslant x \leqslant 2 \\ 3x & \text{when} \quad 2 < x \leqslant 6 \\ 2x + 1 & \text{when} \quad x > 6 \end{cases}$$

Evaluate

(a) $y(0)$ (b) $y(4)$ (c) $y(2)$ (d) $y(7)$

Solution   (a) We require the value of y when $x = 0$. Since 0 lies between -1 and 2 we use the first part of the definition, that is $y = x^2 + 1$. Hence

$$y(0) = 0^2 + 1 = 1$$

(b) We require y when $x = 4$. The second part of the definition must be used because x lies between 2 and 6. Therefore

$$y(4) = 3(4) = 12$$

(c) We require y when $x = 2$. The value $x = 2$ occurs in the first part of the definition. Therefore

$$y(2) = 2^2 + 1 = 5$$

(d) We require y when $x = 7$. The final part of the function must be used. Therefore

$$y(7) = 2(7) + 1 = 15$$

Self-assessment questions 8.2

1. Explain what is meant by a function.

2. Explain the meaning of the terms 'dependent variable' and 'independent variable'.

3. Given $f(x)$, is the statement '$f(1/x)$ means $1/f(x)$' true or false?

4. Give an example of a function $f(x)$ such that $f(2) = f(3)$, that is the outputs for the inputs 2 and 3 are identical.

Exercise 8.2

1. Describe in words each of the following functions:
   (a) $h(t) = 10t$ (b) $g(x) = -x + 2$
   (c) $h(t) = 3t^4$ (d) $f(x) = \dfrac{4}{x^2}$
   (e) $f(x) = 3x^2 - 2x + 9$ (f) $f(x) = 5$
   (g) $f(x) = 0$

2. Describe in words each of the following functions:
   (a) $f(t) = 3t^2 + 2t$ (b) $g(x) = 3x^2 + 2x$
   Comment upon your answers.

3. Write the following functions using mathematical notation:
   (a) The input is cubed and the result is divided by 12.
   (b) The input is added to 3 and the result is squared.
   (c) The input is squared and added to 4 times the input. Finally, 10 is subtracted from the result.
   (d) The input is squared and added to 5. Then the input is divided by this result.
   (e) The input is cubed and then 1 is subtracted from the result.
   (f) 1 is subtracted from the input and the result is squared.

   (g) Twice the input is subtracted from 7 and the result is divided by 4.
   (h) The output is always -13 whatever the value of the input.

4. Given the function $A(n) = n^2 - n + 1$ evaluate
   (a) $A(2)$ (b) $A(3)$ (c) $A(0)$
   (d) $A(-1)$

5. Given $y(x) = (2x - 1)^2$ evaluate
   (a) $y(1)$ (b) $y(-1)$ (c) $y(-3)$
   (d) $y(0.5)$ (e) $y(-0.5)$

6. The function f is given by $f(t) = 4t + 6$. Write expressions for
   (a) $f(t + 1)$ (b) $f(t + 2)$
   (c) $f(t + 1) - f(t)$ (d) $f(t + 2) - f(t)$

7. The function $f(x)$ is defined by $f(x) = 2x^2 - 3$. Write expressions for
   (a) $f(n)$ (b) $f(z)$ (c) $f(t)$ (d) $f(2t)$
   (e) $f\left(\dfrac{1}{z}\right)$ (f) $f\left(\dfrac{3}{n}\right)$ (g) $f(-x)$
   (h) $f(-4x)$ (i) $f(x + 1)$ (j) $f(2x - 1)$

8. Given the function $a(p) = p^2 + 3p + 1$ write an expression for $a(p + 1)$. Verify that $a(p + 1) - a(p) = 2p + 4$.

9. Sometimes the output from one function forms the input to another function. Suppose we have two functions: f given by $f(t) = 2t$, and h given by $h(t) = t + 1$. $f(h(t))$ means that t is input to h, and the output from h is input to f. Evaluate

   (a) $f(3)$ (b) $h(2)$ (c) $f(h(2))$ (d) $h(f(3))$

10. The functions f and h are defined as in Question 9. Write down expressions for

    (a) $f(h(t))$ (b) $h(f(t))$

11. A function is defined by

$$f(x) = \begin{cases} x & 0 \leqslant x < 1 \\ 2 & x = 1 \\ 1 & x > 1 \end{cases}$$

    Evaluate

    (a) $f(0.5)$ (b) $f(1.1)$ (c) $f(1)$

8.3 Composite functions

Sometimes we wish to apply two or more functions, one after the other. The output of one function becomes the input of the next function.

Suppose $f(x) = 2x$ and $g(x) = x + 3$. We note that the function $f(x)$ doubles the input while the function $g(x)$ adds 3 to the input. Now, we let the output of $g(x)$ become the input to $f(x)$. Figure 8.3 illustrates the position.

Figure 8.3
The output of g is the input of f

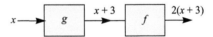

We have

$$g(x) = x + 3$$

$$f(x + 3) = 2(x + 3) = 2x + 6$$

Note that $f(x + 3)$ may be written as $f(g(x))$. Referring to Figure 8.3 we see that the initial input is x and that the final output is $2x + 6$. The functions $g(x)$ and $f(x)$ have been combined. We call $f(g(x))$ a **composite function**. It is composed of the individual functions $f(x)$ and $g(x)$. In this example we have

$$f(g(x)) = 2x + 6$$

WORKED EXAMPLES

8.11   Given $f(x) = 2x$ and $g(x) = x + 3$ find the composite function $g(f(x))$.

Solution   The output of $f(x)$ becomes the input to $g(x)$. Figure 8.4 illustrates this.

Figure 8.4
The composite function $g(f(x))$

We see that

$$g(f(x)) = g(2x)$$
$$= 2x + 3$$

Note that in general $f(g(x))$ and $g(f(x))$ are different functions.

8.12   Given $f(t) = t^2 + 1$, $g(t) = \frac{3}{t}$ and $h(t) = 2t$ determine each of the following composite functions:

(a) $f(g(t))$ (b) $g(h(t))$ (c) $f(h(t))$ (d) $f(g(h(t)))$ (e) $g(f(h(t)))$

Solution   (a) $f(g(t)) = f\left(\dfrac{3}{t}\right) = \left(\dfrac{3}{t}\right)^2 + 1 = \dfrac{9}{t^2} + 1$

(b) $g(h(t)) = g(2t) = \dfrac{3}{2t}$

(c) $f(h(t)) = f(2t) = (2t)^2 + 1 = 4t^2 + 1$

(d) $f(g(h(t))) = f\left(\dfrac{3}{2t}\right)$ using (b)

$$= \left(\dfrac{3}{2t}\right)^2 + 1$$

$$= \dfrac{9}{4t^2} + 1$$

(e) $g(f(h(t))) = g(4t^2 + 1)$ using (c)

$$= \dfrac{3}{4t^2 + 1}$$

Self-assessment questions 8.3

1. Explain the term 'composite function'.

2. Give examples of functions $f(x)$ and $g(x)$ such that $f(g(x))$ and $g(f(x))$ are equal.

Exercise 8.3

1. Given $f(x) = 4x$ and $g(x) = 3x - 2$ find
   (a) $f(g(x))$ (b) $g(f(x))$

2. If $x(t) = t^3$ and $y(t) = 2t$ find
   (a) $y(x(t))$ (b) $x(y(t))$

3. Given $r(x) = \dfrac{1}{2x}$, $s(x) = 3x$ and

   $t(x) = x - 2$ find
   (a) $r(s(x))$ (b) $t(s(x))$ (c) $t(r(s(x)))$
   (d) $r(t(s(x)))$ (e) $r(s(t(x)))$

4. A function can be combined with itself. This is known as **self-composition**. Given $v(t) = 2t + 1$ find
   (a) $v(v(t))$ (b) $v(v(v(t)))$

5. Given $m(t) = (t + 1)^3$, $n(t) = t^2 - 1$ and $p(t) = t^2$ find
   (a) $m(n(t))$ (b) $n(m(t))$ (c) $m(p(t))$
   (d) $p(m(t))$ (e) $n(p(t))$ (f) $p(n(t))$
   (g) $m(n(p(t)))$ (h) $p(p(t))$ (i) $n(n(t))$
   (j) $m(m(t))$

8.4   The inverse of a function

Note that the symbol f^{-1} does not mean $\dfrac{1}{f}$.

We have described a function f as a rule which receives an input, say x, and generates an output, say y. We now consider the reversal of that process, namely finding a function which receives y as input and generates x as the output. If such a function exists it is called the **inverse function** of f. Figure 8.5 illustrates this schematically. The inverse of $f(x)$ is denoted by $f^{-1}(x)$.

Figure 8.5
The inverse of f reverses the effect of f

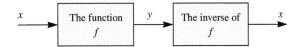

WORKED EXAMPLES

8.13   The functions f and g are defined by

$$f(x) = 2x \qquad g(x) = \frac{x}{2}$$

(a) Verify that f is the inverse of g.
(b) Verify that g is the inverse of f.

Solution   (a) The function g receives an input of x and generates an output of $x/2$; that is, it halves the input. In order to reverse the process, the inverse of g should receive $x/2$ as input and generate x as output. Now consider the function $f(x) = 2x$. This function doubles the input. Hence

$$f\left(\frac{x}{2}\right) = 2\left(\frac{x}{2}\right) = x$$

The function f has received $x/2$ as input and generated x as output. Hence f is the inverse of g. This is shown schematically in Figure 8.6.

Figure 8.6
The function f is the inverse of g

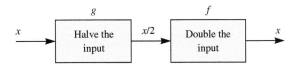

(b) The function f receives x as input and generates $2x$ as output. In order to reverse the process, the inverse of f should receive $2x$ as input and generate x as output. Now $g(x) = x/2$, that is the input is halved, and so

$$g(2x) = \frac{2x}{2} = x$$

Hence g is the inverse of f. This is shown schematically in Figure 8.7.

Figure 8.7
The function g is the
inverse of f

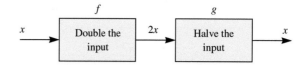

8.14   Find the inverse of the function $f(x) = 3x - 4$.

Solution   The function f multiplies the input by 3 and subtracts 4 from the result. To reverse the process, the inverse function, g say, must add 4 to the input and then divide the result by 3. Hence

$$g(x) = \frac{x + 4}{3}$$

8.15   Find the inverse of $h(t) = -\frac{1}{2}t + 5$.

Solution   The function h multiplies the input by $-\frac{1}{2}$ and then adds 5 to the result. Therefore the inverse function, g say, must subtract 5 from the input and then divide the result by $-\frac{1}{2}$. Hence

$$g(t) = \frac{(t - 5)}{-1/2} = -2(t - 5) = -2t + 10$$

There is an algebraic method of finding an inverse function that is often easier to apply. Suppose we wish to find the inverse of the function $f(x) = 6 - 2x$. We let

$$y = 6 - 2x$$

and then transpose this for x. This gives

$$x = \frac{6 - y}{2}$$

Finally, we interchange x and y to give $y = (6 - x)/2$. This is the required inverse function. To summarise these stages:

Key point   To find the inverse of $y = f(x)$,

- transpose the formula to make x the subject

- interchange x and y

The result is the required inverse function.

We shall meet some functions that do not have an inverse function. For example, consider the function $f(x) = x^2$. If 3 is the input, the output is 9. Now if -3 is the input, the output will also be 9 since $(-3)^2 = 9$. In order to reverse this process an inverse function would have to take an input of 9 and produce outputs of both 3 and -3. However, this contradicts the definition of a function, which states that a function must have only *one* output for a given input. We say that $f(x) = x^2$ does not have an inverse function.

Self-assessment questions 8.4

1. Explain what is meant by the inverse of a function.

2. Explain why the function $f(x) = 4x^4$ does not possess an inverse function.

Exercise 8.4

1. Find the inverse of each of the following functions:
   (a) $f(x) = 3x$ (b) $f(x) = \dfrac{x}{4}$
   (c) $f(x) = x + 1$ (d) $f(x) = x - 3$
   (e) $f(x) = 3 - x$ (f) $f(x) = 2x + 6$
   (g) $f(x) = 7 - 3x$ (h) $f(x) = \dfrac{1}{x}$
   (i) $f(x) = \dfrac{3}{x}$ (j) $f(x) = -\dfrac{3}{4x}$

2. Find the inverse, $f^{-1}(x)$, when $f(x)$ is given by
   (a) $6x$ (b) $6x + 1$ (c) $x + 6$
   (d) $\dfrac{x}{6}$ (e) $\dfrac{6}{x}$

3. Find the inverse, $g^{-1}(t)$, when $g(t)$ is given by
   (a) $3t + 1$ (b) $\dfrac{1}{3t + 1}$ (c) t^3
   (d) $3t^3$ (e) $3t^3 + 1$ (f) $\dfrac{3}{t^3 + 1}$

4. The functions $g(t)$ and $h(t)$ are defined by
   $$g(t) = 2t - 1, h(t) = 4t + 3$$
   Find
   (a) the inverse of $h(t)$, that is $h^{-1}(t)$
   (b) the inverse of $g(t)$, that is $g^{-1}(t)$
   (c) $g^{-1}(h^{-1}(t))$ (d) $h(g(t))$
   (e) the inverse of $h(g(t))$

   What observations do you make from (c) and (e)?

Challenge Exercise 8

1. $x(t)$ and $y(t)$ are both linear functions of t, that is, $x(t) = at + b$, $y(t) = ct + d$ where a, b, c and d are constants. Show that $y^{-1}(x^{-1}(t))$ is identical to the inverse of $x(y(t))$.

Test and assignment exercises 8

1. Given $r(t) = t^2 - t/2 + 4$ evaluate
   (a) $r(0)$ (b) $r(-1)$ (c) $r(2)$ (d) $r(3.6)$ (e) $r(-4.6)$

2. A function is defined as $h(t) = t^2 - 7$.
   (a) State the dependent variable. (b) State the independent variable.

3. Given the functions $a(x) = x^2 + 1$ and $b(x) = 2x + 1$ write expressions for

   (a) $a(\alpha)$ (b) $b(t)$ (c) $a(2x)$ (d) $b\left(\dfrac{x}{3}\right)$ (e) $a(x + 1)$

   (f) $b(x + h)$ (g) $b(x - h)$ (h) $a(b(x))$ (i) $b(a(x))$

4. Find the inverse of each of the following functions:

   (a) $f(x) = \pi - x$ (b) $h(t) = \dfrac{t}{3} + 2$ (c) $r(n) = \dfrac{1}{n}$ (d) $r(n) = \dfrac{1}{n - 1}$

   (e) $r(n) = \dfrac{2}{n - 1}$ (f) $r(n) = \dfrac{a}{n - b}$ where a and b are constants

5. Given $A(n) = n^2 + n - 6$ find expressions for

   (a) $A(n + 1)$ (b) $A(n - 1)$
   (c) $2A(n + 1) - A(n) + A(n - 1)$

6. Find $h^{-1}(x)$ when $h(x)$ is given by

   (a) $\dfrac{x + 1}{3}$ (b) $\dfrac{3}{x + 1}$ (c) $\dfrac{x + 1}{x}$ (d) $\dfrac{x}{x + 1}$

7. Given $v(t) = 4t - 2$ find
   (a) $v^{-1}(t)$ (b) $v(v(t))$

8. Given $h(x) = 9x - 6$ and $g(x) = \dfrac{1}{3x}$ find
   (a) $h(g(x))$ (b) $g(h(x))$

9. Given $f(x) = (x + 1)^2$, $g(x) = 4x$ and $h(x) = x - 1$ find
   (a) $f(g(x))$ (b) $g(f(x))$ (c) $f(h(x))$ (d) $h(f(x))$ (e) $g(h(x))$
   (f) $h(g(x))$ (g) $f(g(h(x)))$ (h) $g(h(f(x)))$

10. Given $x(t) = t^3$, $y(t) = \dfrac{1}{t + 1}$ and $z(t) = 3t - 1$ find

    (a) $y(x(t))$ (b) $y(z(t))$ (c) $x(y(z(t)))$ (d) $z(y(x(t)))$

11. Write each of the following functions using mathematical notation:
    (a) The input is multiplied by 7.
    (b) Five times the square of the input is subtracted from twice the cube of the input.
    (c) The output is 6.
    (d) The input is added to the reciprocal of the input.
    (e) The input is multiplied by 11 and then 6 is subtracted from this. Finally, 9 is divided by this result.

12. Find the inverse of

    $$f(x) = \dfrac{x + 1}{x - 1}$$

Tables and charts

9

Objectives: This chapter:

- explains the distinction between discrete and continuous data

- shows how raw data can be organised using a tally chart

- explains what is meant by a frequency distribution and a relative frequency distribution

- shows how data can be represented in the form of bar charts, pie charts, pictograms and histograms

9.1 Introduction to data

In the modern world, information from a wide range of sources is gathered, presented and interpreted. Most newspapers, television news programmes and documentaries contain vast numbers of facts and figures concerning almost every aspect of life, including environmental issues, the lengths of hospital waiting lists, crime statistics and economic performance indicators. Information such as this, which is gathered by carrying out surveys and doing research, is known as **data.**

Sometimes data must take on a value from a specific set of numbers, and no other values are possible. For example, the number of children in a family must be 0, 1, 2, 3, 4 and so on, and no intermediate values are allowed. It is impossible to have 3.32 children, say. Such data is said to be **discrete.** Other examples of discrete data include:

- the number of car thefts in a city in one week – this must be 0, 1, 2, 3 and so on. You cannot have three-and-a-half thefts.

- shoe sizes – these can be $\ldots, 3\frac{1}{2}, 4, 4\frac{1}{2}, 5, 5\frac{1}{2}, 6, 6\frac{1}{2}, 7$ and so on. You cannot have a shoe size of 9.82.

Sometimes data can take on *any* value within a specified range. Such data is called **continuous.** The volume of liquid in a 1 litre jug can take any value from 0 to 1 litre. The lifespan of an electric light bulb could be any non-negative value.

Frequently data is presented in the form of tables and charts, the intention being to make the information readily understandable. When data is first collected, and before it is processed in any way, it is known as **raw data.** For example, in a test the mathematics marks out of 10 of a group of 30 students are

$$7 \quad 5 \quad 5 \quad 8 \quad 9 \quad 10 \quad 9 \quad 10 \quad 7 \quad 8 \quad 6 \quad 3 \quad 5 \quad 9 \quad 6$$
$$10 \quad 8 \quad 8 \quad 7 \quad 8 \quad 6 \quad 7 \quad 8 \quad 8 \quad 10 \quad 9 \quad 4 \quad 5 \quad 9 \quad 8$$

This is raw data. To try to make sense of this data it is helpful to find out how many students scored each particular mark. This can be done by means of a **tally chart.** To produce this we write down in a column all the possible marks, in order. We then go through the raw data and indicate the occurrence of each mark with a vertical line or tally like /. Every time a fifth tally is recorded this is shown by striking through the previous four, as in ⦀⃥. This makes counting up the tallies particularly easy. The tallies for all the marks are shown in Table 9.1. The number of occurrences of each mark is called its **frequency,** and the frequencies can be found from the number of tallies. We see that the tally chart is a useful way of organising the raw data into a form that will enable us to answer questions and obtain useful information about it.

Table 9.1
Tally chart for mathematics marks

Mark	Tally	Frequency
0		0
1		0
2		0
3	/	1
4	/	1
5	////	4
6	///	3
7	////	4
8	⦀⃥ ///	8
9	⦀⃥	5
10	////	4
Total		30

Nowadays much of the tedium of producing tally charts for very large amounts of data can be avoided using computer programs available specifically for this purpose.

Self-assessment questions 9.1

1. Explain the distinction between discrete data and continuous data. Give a new example of each.

2. Explain the purpose of a tally chart.

Exercise 9.1

1. State whether each of the following is an example of discrete data or continuous data:
   (a) the number of matches found in a matchbox
   (b) the percentage of sulphur dioxide found in an air sample taken above a city
   (c) the number of peas in a packet of frozen peas
   (d) the radius of a ball bearing
   (e) the weight of a baby
   (f) the number of students in a particular type of accommodation
   (g) the weight of a soil sample
   (h) the temperature of a patient in hospital
   (i) the number of telephone calls received by an answering machine during one day

2. Twenty-five people were asked to state their year of birth. The information given was

   1975 1975 1974 1974 1975 1976 1976 1974 1972 1973 1973 1970 1975
   1975 1973 1970 1975 1974 1975 1974 1970 1973 1974 1974 1975

   Produce a tally chart to organise this data and state the frequency of occurrence of each year of birth.

9.2 Frequency tables and distributions

Data is often presented in a **table.** For example, in a recent survey, 1000 students were asked to state the type of accommodation in which they lived during term time. The data gathered is given in Table 9.2. As we saw from the work in the previous section, the number of occurrences of each entry in the table is known as its **frequency.** So, for example, the frequency of students in private rented accommodation is 250. The table summarises the various frequencies and is known as a **frequency distribution.**

A **relative frequency distribution** is found by expressing each frequency as a proportion of the total frequency.

Table 9.2
Frequency distribution

Type of accommodation	Number of students
Hall of residence	675
Parental home	50
Private rented	250
Other	25
Total	1000

Key point The relative frequency is found by dividing a frequency by the total frequency.

In this example, because the total frequency is 1000, the relative frequency is easy to calculate. The number of students living at their parental home is 50 out of a total of 1000. Therefore the relative frequency of this group of students is $\frac{50}{1000}$ or 0.050. Table 9.3 shows the relative frequency distribution of student accommodation. Note that the relative frequencies always sum to 1.

Table 9.3
Relative frequency
distribution

Type of accommodation	Number of students	Relative frequency
Hall of residence	675	0.675
Parental home	50	0.050
Private rented	250	0.250
Other	25	0.025
Total	1000	1.000

It is sometimes helpful to express the frequencies as percentages. This is done by multiplying each relative frequency by 100, which gives the results shown in Table 9.4. We see from this that 5% of students questioned live at their parental home.

Table 9.4
Frequencies expressed as
percentages

Type of accommodation	Number of students	Relative frequency × 100
Hall of residence	675	67.5%
Parental home	50	5.0%
Private rented	250	25.0%
Other	25	2.5%
Total	1000	100%

| Key point | A frequency can be expressed as a percentage by multiplying its relative frequency by 100. |

WORKED EXAMPLE

9.1   In 1988 there were 4320 areas throughout the world that were designated as national parks. Table 9.5 is a frequency distribution showing how these parks are distributed in different parts of the world.

(a) Express this data as a relative frequency distribution and also in terms of percentages.

(b) What percentage of the world's national parks are in Africa?

Table 9.5
The number of national parks throughout the world

Region	Number of national parks
Africa	486
N. America	587
S. America	315
Former Soviet Union	168
Asia	960
Europe	1032
Oceania	767
Antarctica	5
Total	4320

Solution

Table 9.6
The number of national parks throughout the world

Region	Number	Relative frequency	Rel. freq. × 100
Africa	486	0.1125	11.25%
N. America	587	0.1359	13.59%
S. America	315	0.0729	7.29%
Former Soviet Union	168	0.0389	3.89%
Asia	960	0.2222	22.22%
Europe	1032	0.2389	23.89%
Oceania	767	0.1775	17.75%
Antarctica	5	0.0012	0.12%
Total	4320	1.000	100%

(a) The relative frequencies are found by expressing each frequency as a proportion of the total. For example, Europe has 1032 national parks out of a total of 4320, and so its relative frequency is $\frac{1032}{4320} = 0.2389$. Figures for the other regions have been calculated and are shown in Table 9.6. To express a relative frequency as a percentage it is multiplied by 100. Thus we find that Europe has 23.89% of the world's national parks. The percentages for the other regions are also shown in Table 9.6.

(b) We note from Table 9.6 that 11.25% of the world's national parks are in Africa.

When dealing with large amounts of data it is usual to group the data into classes. For example, in an environmental experiment the weights in grams of 30 soil samples were measured using a balance. We could list all 30 weights here but such a long list of data is cumbersome. Instead, we have already grouped the data into several weight ranges or **classes.** Table 9.7 shows the number of samples in each class. Such a table is called a **grouped frequency distribution.**

Table 9.7
Grouped frequency distribution

Weight range (grams)	Number of samples in that range
100–109	5
110–119	8
120–129	11
130–139	5
140–149	1
Total	30

A disadvantage of grouping the data in this way is that information about individual weights is lost. However, this disadvantage is usually outweighed by having a more compact set of data that is easier to work with. There are five samples that lie in the first class, eight samples in the second and so on. For the first class, the numbers 100 and 109 are called **class limits,** the smaller number being the **lower class limit** and the larger being the **upper class limit.** Theoretically, the class 100–109 includes all weights from 99.5 g up to but not including 109.5 g. These numbers are called the **class boundaries.** In practice the class boundaries are found by adding the upper class limit of one class to the lower limit of the next class and dividing by 2. The **class width** is the difference between the larger class boundary and the smaller. The class 100–109 has width $109.5 - 99.5 = 10$. We do not know the actual values of the weights in each class. Should we require an estimate, the best we can do is use the value in the middle of the class, known as the class **midpoint.** The midpoint of the first class is 104.5, the midpoint of the second class is 114.5 and so on. The midpoint can be found by adding half the class width to the lower class boundary.

WORKED EXAMPLE

9.2   The systolic blood pressure in millimetres of mercury of 20 workers was recorded to the nearest millimetre. The data collected was as follows:

121   123   124   129   130   119   129   124   119   121   122   124

124   128   129   136   120   119   121   136

(a) Group this data into classes 115–119, 120–124, and so on.

(b) State the class limits of the first three classes.

(c) State the class boundaries of the first three classes.

(d) What is the class width of the third class?

(e) What is the midpoint of the third class?

Solution   (a) To group the data a tally chart is used as shown in Table 9.8.

Table 9.8
Tally chart for blood pressures

Pressure (mm mercury)	Tally	Frequency
115–119	///	3
120–124	HHT HHT	10
125–129	////	4
130–134	/	1
135–139	//	2
Total		20

(b) The class limits of the first class are 115 and 119; those of the second class are 120 and 124; those of the third are 125 and 129.

(c) Theoretically, the class 115–119 will contain all blood pressures between 114.5 and 119.5 and so the class boundaries of the first class are 114.5 and 119.5. The class boundaries of the second class are 119.5 and 124.5, and those of the third class are 124.5 and 129.5.

(d) The upper class boundary of the third class is 129.5. The lower class boundary is 124.5. The difference between these values gives the class width, that is $129.5 - 124.5 = 5$.

(e) The midpoint of the third class is found by adding half the class width to the lower class boundary, that is $2.5 + 124.5 = 127$.

Self-assessment questions 9.2

1. Why is it often useful to present data in the form of a *grouped* frequency distribution?

2. Explain the distinction between class boundaries and class limits.

3. How is the class width calculated?

4. How is the class midpoint calculated?

Exercise 9.2

1. The age of each patient over the age of 14 visiting a doctor's practice in one day was recorded as follows:

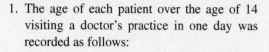

18   18   76   15   72   45   48   62   21
27   45   43   28   19   17   37   35   34
23   25   46   56   32   18   23   34   32
56   29   43

(a) Use a tally chart to produce a grouped frequency distribution with age groupings 15–19, 20–24, 25–29, and so on.

(b) What is the relative frequency of patients in the age group 70–74?

(c) What is the relative frequency of patients aged 70 and over?

(d) Express the number of patients in the age group 25–29 as a percentage.

2. Consider the following table, which shows the lifetimes, to the nearest hour, of 100 energy saving light bulbs.

(a) If a light bulb has a life of 5499.4 hours, into which class will it be put?

(b) If a light bulb has a life of 5499.8 hours, into which class will it be put?

(c) State the class boundaries of each class.

(d) Find the class width.

(e) State the class midpoint of each class.

Lifetime (hours)	Frequency
5000–5499	6
5500–5999	32
6000–6499	58
6500–6999	4
Total	100

3. The percentages of 60 students in an Information Technology test are given as follows:

45   92   81   76   51   46   82   65   61
19   62   58   72   65   66   97   61   57
63   93   61   46   47   61   56   45   39
47   55   58   81   71   52   38   53   59
82   92   87   86   51   29   19   79   55
18   53   29   87   87   77   85   67   89
17   29   86   57   59   57

Form a frequency distribution by drawing up a tally chart using classes 0–9, 10–19 and so on.

4. The data in the table opposite gives the radius of 20 ball bearings. State the class boundaries of the second class and find the class width.

Radius (mm)	Frequency
20.56–20.58	3
20.59–20.61	6
20.62–20.64	8
20.65–20.67	3

9.3   Bar charts, pie charts, pictograms and histograms

In a **bar chart** information is represented by rectangles or bars. The bars may be drawn horizontally or vertically. The length of each bar corresponds to a frequency.

The data given earlier in Table 9.2. concerning student accommodation is presented in the form of a horizontal bar chart in Figure 9.1. Note that the scale on the horizontal axis must be uniform, that is it must be evenly spaced, and that the type of accommodation is clearly identified on each bar. The bar chart must be given a title to explain the information that is being presented.

Figure 9.1
Horizontal bar chart showing student accommodation

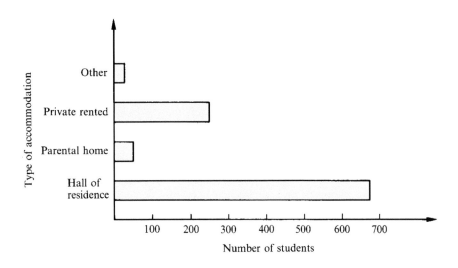

WORKED EXAMPLE

9.3   A reproduction antique furniture manufacturer has been producing pine wardrobes for the past six years. The number of wardrobes sold each year is given in Table 9.9. Produce a vertical bar chart to illustrate this information.

Table 9.9
Wardrobes sold

Year	Number sold
2014	15
2015	16
2016	20
2017	20
2018	24
2019	30

Solution   The information is presented in the form of a vertical bar chart in Figure 9.2.

Figure 9.2
Vertical bar chart showing
the number of wardrobes
sold each year

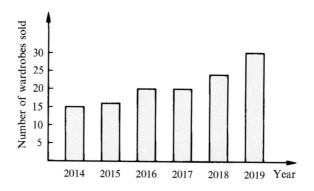

In a **pie chart,** a circular 'pie' is divided into a number of portions, with each portion, or **sector,** of the pie representing a different category. The whole pie represents all categories together. The size of a particular portion must represent the number in its category, and this is done by dividing the circle proportionately.

WORKED EXAMPLE

9.4   A sample of 360 people were asked to state their favourite flavour of potato crisp: 75 preferred 'plain' crisps, 120 preferred 'cheese and onion', 90 preferred 'salt and vinegar', and the remaining 75 preferred 'beef'. Draw a pie chart to present this data.

Solution   All categories together, that is all 360 people asked, make up the whole pie. Because there are 360° in a circle this makes the pie chart particularly easy to draw. A sector of angle 75° will represent 'plain crisps', a sector of 120° will represent 'cheese and onion' and so on. The pie chart is shown in Figure 9.3.

Figure 9.3
Pie chart showing
preferred flavour of crisps
of 360 people

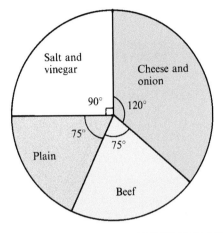

The pie chart in the previous worked example was simple to draw because the total number of all categories was 360, the same as the number of degrees in a circle. Let us now see how to deal with a situation where this is not the case. First each relative frequency is found and then this is multiplied by 360. The result is the angle, in degrees, of the corresponding sector.

Key point   The angle, in degrees, of each sector in a pie chart is found by multiplying the corresponding relative frequency by 360. This gives the angle of each sector.

WORKED EXAMPLE

9.5   Five hundred students were asked to state how they usually travelled to and from their place of study. The results are given in Table 9.10. Present this information in a pie chart.

Table 9.10
Means of travel

Means of travel	Frequency f
Bus	50
Walk	180
Cycle	200
Car	40
Other	30
Total	500

Solution   To find the angle of each sector of the pie chart we first find the corresponding relative frequencies. Recall that this is done by dividing each frequency by the total, 500. Then each relative frequency is multiplied by 360. The results are shown in Table 9.11. The table gives the required angles. The pie chart can then be drawn. This is shown in Figure 9.4.

Table 9.11
Means of travel

Means of travel	Frequency f	Rel. freq. $f/500$	Rel. freq. $\times$ 360
Bus	50	$\frac{50}{500}$	$\frac{50}{500} \times 360 = 36.0°$
Walk	180	$\frac{180}{500}$	$\frac{180}{500} \times 360 = 129.6°$
Cycle	200	$\frac{200}{500}$	$\frac{200}{500} \times 360 = 144.0°$
Car	40	$\frac{40}{500}$	$\frac{40}{500} \times 360 = 28.8°$
Other	30	$\frac{30}{500}$	$\frac{30}{500} \times 360 = 21.6°$
Total	500		360°

Figure 9.4
Pie chart showing how
students travel to work

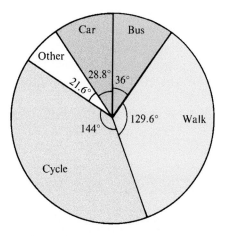

A **pictogram** uses a picture to represent data in an eye-catching way. There are many ways to produce pictograms but generally the number of objects drawn represents the number of items in a particular category. This is a common form of representation popular on television when the viewer sees the information for only a few seconds.

WORKED EXAMPLE

9.6   The number of hours of sunshine in each of the four months January, April, July and October in the holiday resort of Torquay is given in Table 9.12. Show this information using a pictogram. Use one 'sun' to represent 30 hours of sunshine.

Table 9.12
Pictogram showing hours of sunshine.

Month	Number of hours
January	120
April	270
July	240
October	180

Solution   The pictogram is shown in Figure 9.5.

Figure 9.5
Pictogram showing hours of sunshine in each of four months.

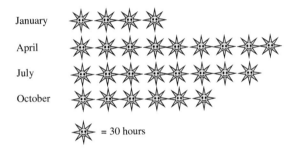

A **histogram** is often used to illustrate data that is continuous or has been grouped. It is similar to a vertical bar chart in that it is drawn by constructing vertical rectangles. However, in a histogram it is the *area* of each rectangle, and not its length, that is proportional to the frequency of each class. When all class widths are the same this point is not important and you can assume that the length of a rectangle represents the frequency. When class widths vary, then the length of a rectangle is given by the 'frequency density', not the frequency. Class boundaries and not class limits must be used on the horizontal axis to distinguish one class from the next. Consider the following examples.

WORKED EXAMPLE

9.7   The heights, to the nearest centimetre, of 100 students are given in Table 9.13.

Table 9.13
Height of 100 students

Height (cm)	Frequency
164–165	4
166–167	8
168–169	10
170–171	27
172–173	30
174–175	10
176–177	6
178–179	5
Total	100

(a) State the class limits of the second class.

(b) Identify the class boundaries of the first class and the last class.

(c) In which class would a student whose actual height is 167.4 cm be placed?

(d) In which class would a student whose actual height is 167.5 cm be placed?

(e) Draw a histogram to depict this data.

Solution

(a) The lower class limit of the second class is 166 cm. The upper class limit is 167 cm.

(b) The class boundaries of the first class are 163.5 cm and 165.5 cm. The class boundaries of the last class are 177.5 cm and 179.5 cm.

(c) A student with height 167.4 cm will have his height recorded to the nearest centimetre as 167. He will be placed in the class 166–167.

(d) A student with height 167.5 cm will have her height recorded to the nearest centimetre as 168. She will be placed in the class 168–169.

(e) The histogram is shown in Figure 9.6. Note that the class boundaries are used on the horizontal axis to distinguish one class from the next. The area of each rectangle is proportional to the frequency of each class.

Figure 9.6
Histogram showing the distribution of heights of 100 students

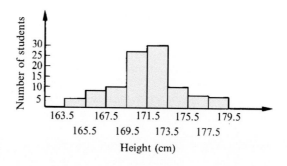

Note that all the class widths are the same, namely 2 cm. Since all class widths are identical then the vertical axis of the histogram is simply the frequency, that is, the number of students.

WORKED EXAMPLE

9.8   The heights of 100 adults are recorded to the nearest cm and the results are shown in the frequency distribution in Table 9.14.

Table 9.14
Heights of 100 adults

Height, h, (cm)	Frequency
$140 \leqslant h < 155$	2
$155 \leqslant h < 160$	6
$160 \leqslant h < 165$	14
$165 \leqslant h < 175$	26
$175 \leqslant h < 185$	29
$185 \leqslant h < 190$	17
$190 \leqslant h < 210$	6

Note that in this distribution the class boundaries are given. For example, the class boundaries of the first class are 140 cm (lower) and 155 cm (upper).
Represent this frequency distribution as a histogram.

Solution   Note that the class widths vary from class to class. Table 9.15 shows the class widths.

Table 9.15
Class widths vary from class to class

Height, h, (cm)	Frequency	Class width (cm)
$140 \leqslant h < 155$	2	15
$155 \leqslant h < 160$	6	5
$160 \leqslant h < 165$	14	5
$165 \leqslant h < 175$	26	10
$175 \leqslant h < 185$	29	10
$185 \leqslant h < 190$	17	5
$190 \leqslant h < 210$	6	20

Since the class widths vary, the vertical axis of the histogram must be 'frequency density', not simply frequency. The 'frequency density' is found from

$$\text{Frequency density} = \frac{\text{Frequency}}{\text{Class width}}$$

Table 9.16 shows the frequency density for each class.

Table 9.16
The frequency density is found by dividing 'Frequency' by 'Class width'

Height, h, (cm)	Frequency	Class width (cm)	Frequency density
$140 \leqslant h < 155$	2	15	2/15 = 0.13
$155 \leqslant h < 160$	6	5	6/5 = 1.2
$160 \leqslant h < 165$	14	5	14/5 = 2.8
$165 \leqslant h < 175$	26	10	26/10 = 2.6
$175 \leqslant h < 185$	29	10	29/10 = 2.9
$185 \leqslant h < 190$	17	5	17/5 = 3.4
$190 \leqslant h < 210$	6	20	6/20 = 0.3

The width of each rectangle of the histogram is the class width. The height of each rectangle is the frequency density. Figure 9.7 shows the histogram.

Figure 9.7
Histogram for the frequency distribution of Table 9.14

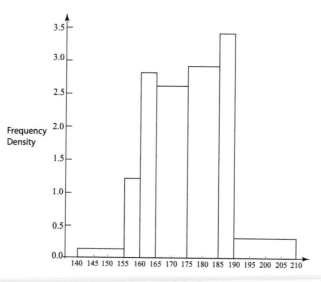

Height (cm)

Key point

When class widths vary the frequency density is used for the vertical axis of the histogram. Frequency density is found from

$$\text{Frequency density} = \frac{\text{Frequency}}{\text{Class width}}$$

WORKED EXAMPLE

9.9   A parcel delivery company weighs each parcel it receives on a particular day. The results are given in the frequency distribution in Table 9.17.

Table 9.17
Weights of parcels

Weight, w, (kg)	Frequency
$0 \leqslant w < 0.25$	43
$0.25 \leqslant w < 0.5$	76
$0.5 \leqslant w < 1.0$	61
$1.0 \leqslant w < 2.0$	55
$2.0 \leqslant w < 3.0$	41
$3.0 \leqslant w < 5.0$	30
$5.0 \leqslant w < 10$	21

Draw a histogram for Table 9.17.

Solution   We note that there is a variety of class widths and so we calculate the frequency density for each class. The results are shown in Table 9.18.

Table 9.18
Class width and frequency density for Table 9.17

Weight, w, (kg)	Frequency	Class width (kg)	Frequency density
$0 \leqslant w < 0.25$	43	0.25	$43/0.25 = 172$
$0.25 \leqslant w < 0.5$	76	0.25	$76/0.25 = 304$
$0.5 \leqslant w < 1.0$	61	0.5	$61/0.5 = 122$
$1.0 \leqslant w < 2.0$	55	1	$55/1 = 55$
$2.0 \leqslant w < 3.0$	41	1	$41/1 = 41$
$3.0 \leqslant w < 5.0$	30	2	$30/2 = 15$
$5.0 \leqslant w < 10$	21	5	$21/5 = 4.2$

The histogram is constructed using frequency density on the vertical axis and the class boundaries on the horizontal axis. The histogram is shown in Figure 9.8.

Figure 9.8
Histogram with varying
class widths

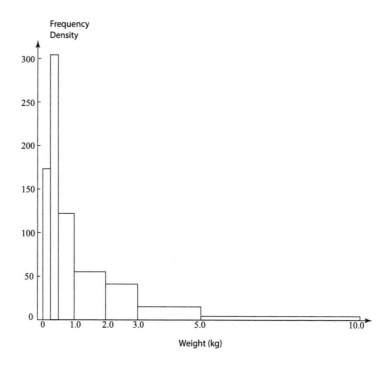

Self-assessment questions 9.3

1. There is an important distinction between a histogram and a vertical bar chart. Can you explain this?

2. Give one advantage and one disadvantage of using a pictogram to represent data.

3. On a histogram the class boundaries are used on the horizontal axis to distinguish one class from the next. Why do you think class boundaries as opposed to class limits are used?

Exercise 9.3

1. A local council wants to produce a leaflet explaining how the council tax is spent. For every one pound spent, 40p went to Education, 15p went to the Police, 15p went to Cleansing and Refuse, 20p went to Highways and the remaining 10p went to a variety of other services. Show this information (a) using a pie chart, and (b) using a pictogram.

2. The composition of the atmosphere of the Earth is 78% nitrogen, 21% oxygen and 1% other gases. Draw a pie chart to show this information.

3. An insurance company keeps records on the distribution of the amount of small claims for theft it receives. Amounts are given to the nearest pound. This information is given in the following table.

Amount (£)	Frequency
0–99	5
100–199	8
200–299	16
300–399	24
400–499	26

(a) State the class boundaries.
(b) In which class would a claim for £199.75 be placed?
(c) Draw a histogram to show this information.

4. A railway users group records the length of time that trains are late at a particular station. Results are given in the following table.

Lateness of train, L, (mins)	Frequency
$0 \leqslant L < 1$	51
$1 \leqslant L < 2$	36
$2 \leqslant L < 3$	39
$3 \leqslant L < 4$	17
$4 \leqslant L < 5$	10
$5 \leqslant L < 10$	16
$10 \leqslant L < 15$	4
$15 \leqslant L < 30$	1
$30 \leqslant L < 60$	2

(a) State the class boundaries of the first and last class.
(b) Calculate the class width of each class and the corresponding frequency density.
(c) Draw the histogram.

Test and assignment exercises 9

1. State whether the following are examples of discrete or continuous data:
   (a) the temperature of a furnace
   (b) the number of goals scored in a football match
   (c) the amount of money in a worker's wage packet at the end of the week

2. A group of students were interviewed to obtain information on their termly expenditure. On average, for every pound spent, 60p was spent on accommodation, fuel etc., 25p was spent on food, 10p was spent on entertainment and the remainder on a variety of other items. Draw a pie chart to show this expenditure.

3. Forty lecturers were asked to state which newspaper they bought most regularly. The results were: *Guardian*, 15; *Independent*, 8; *The Times*, 2; *Daily Express*, 7; *Daily Mail*, 2; None, 6. Produce a pie chart to show this data.

4. The percentage of total body weight formed by various parts of the body of a newborn baby is as follows: muscles, 26%; skeleton, 17%; skin, 20%; heart, lungs etc., 11%; remainder, 26%. Depict this information (a) on a pie chart, (b) using a bar chart.

5. The following marks were obtained by 27 students in a test. Draw up a frequency distribution by means of a tally chart.

   5 4 6 2 9 1 10 10 5 5 6 5 5 9 8 7 9 6 7 6 8 7 6 9 8 8 7

6. The number of cars sold by a major manufacturer of luxury cars in the last 10 years is given in the table below. Show this data on a horizontal bar chart.

Year	Number
2006	2800
2007	1500
2008	1425
2009	1300
2010	1560
2011	1870
2012	2100
2013	2340
2014	2610
2015	2780

7. The table below shows the frequency distribution of the lifetimes in hours of 100 light bulbs tested.
   (a) State the class limits of the first and second classes.
   (b) State the class boundaries of all classes.
   (c) Determine each class width and midpoint.
   (d) Draw a histogram for this frequency distribution.

Lifetime (hours)	Frequency
600–699	13
700–799	25
800–899	32
900–999	10
1000–1099	15
1100–1199	5

8. In each year from 2014 to 2019 the numbers of visitors to a museum were respectively 12000, 13000, 14500, 18000, 18000 and 17500. Show this information in a pictogram.

9. The length of calls made to a utility call-centre are measured over a 1 hour period. Results are shown in the following table.

Length of call, L, (mins)	Frequency
$0 \leqslant L < 1$	42
$1 \leqslant L < 2$	61
$2 \leqslant L < 3$	53
$3 \leqslant L < 5$	42
$5 \leqslant L < 10$	56
$10 \leqslant L < 15$	48

Draw a histogram for this table.

Statistics

Objectives: This chapter:

- ■ introduces the three common averages – mean, median and mode – and shows how to calculate them

- ■ explains what is meant by the variance and standard deviation and shows how to calculate them

---

10.1 Introduction

In the previous chapter we outlined how data gathered from a range of sources can be represented. In order to get the most out of such data and be able to interpret it sensibly and reliably, techniques have been developed for its analysis. **Statistics** is the name given to this science. One important statistical quantity is an 'average', the purpose of which is to represent a whole set of data by a single number that in some way represents the set. This chapter explains three types of average and shows how to calculate them. Finally the 'variance' and 'standard deviation' are introduced. These are numbers that describe how widely the data is spread.

10.2 Averages: the mean, median and mode

When presented with a large amount of data it is often useful to ask 'is there a single number that typifies the data?' For example, following an examination taken by a large number of candidates, examiners may be dealing with hundreds of examination scripts. The marks on these will vary from those with very poor marks to those with very high or even top marks. In order to judge whether the group of students as a whole found the examination difficult, the examiner may be asked to provide a single value that gives a measure of how well the students have performed. Such a value is called an **average.** In statistics there are three important averages: the arithmetic mean, the median and the mode.

The arithmetic mean

The **arithmetic mean**, or simply the **mean**, of a set of values is found by adding up all the values and dividing the result by the total number of values in the set. It is given by the following formula:

Key point

$$\text{mean} = \frac{\text{sum of the values}}{\text{total number of values}}$$

WORKED EXAMPLES

10.1   Eight students sit a mathematics test and their marks out of 10 are 4, 6, 6, 7, 7, 7, 8 and 10. Find the mean mark.

Solution   The sum of the marks is $4 + 6 + 6 + 7 + 7 + 7 + 8 + 10 = 55$. The total number of values is 8. Therefore,

$$\text{mean} = \frac{\text{sum of the values}}{\text{total number of values}} = \frac{55}{8} = 6.875$$

The examiner can quote 6.875 out of 10 as the 'average mark' of the group of students.

10.2   In a hospital a patient's body temperature is recorded every hour for six hours. Find the mean temperature over the six-hour period if the six temperatures, in °C, were

36.5   36.8   36.9   36.9   36.9   37.0

Solution   To find the mean temperature the sum of all six values is found and the result is divided by 6. That is,

$$\text{mean} = \frac{36.5 + 36.8 + 36.9 + 36.9 + 36.9 + 37.0}{6}$$

$$= \frac{221.0}{6} = 36.83 \,°C$$

In more advanced work we make use of a formula for the mean that requires knowledge of some special notation. Suppose we have n values and we call these x_1, x_2, x_3 and so on up to x_n. The mean of these values is given the symbol

$\bar{x}$, pronounced 'x bar'. To calculate the mean we must add up these values and divide by n, that is

$$\text{mean} = \bar{x} = \frac{x_1 + x_2 + x_3 + \cdots + x_n}{n}$$

A notation is often used to shorten this formula. In mathematics, the Greek letter sigma, written $\sum$, stands for a sum. The sum $x_1 + x_2$ is written

$$\sum_{i=1}^{2} x_i$$

and the sum $x_1 + x_2 + x_3 + x_4$ is written

$$\sum_{i=1}^{4} x_i$$

Note that i runs through all integer values from 1 to n.

where the values below and above the sigma sign give the first and last values in the sum. Similarly $x_1 + x_2 + x_3 + \cdots + x_n$ is written $\sum_{i=1}^{n} x_i$. Using this notation, the formula for the mean can be written in the following way:

Key point

$$\text{mean} = \bar{x} = \frac{\sum_{i=1}^{n} x_i}{n}$$

There is a further treatment of sigma notation.

WORKED EXAMPLES

10.3   Express the following in sigma notation:

(a) $x_1 + x_2 + x_3 + \cdots + x_8 + x_9$

(b) $x_{10} + x_{11} + \cdots + x_{100}$

Solution   (a) $x_1 + x_2 + x_3 + \cdots + x_8 + x_9 = \sum_{i=1}^{9} x_i$

(b) $x_{10} + x_{11} + \cdots + x_{100} = \sum_{i=10}^{100} x_i$

10.4   Find the mean of the values $x_1 = 5$, $x_2 = 7$, $x_3 = 13$, $x_4 = 21$ and $x_5 = 29$.

Solution   The number of values equals 5, so we let $n = 5$. The sum of the values is

$$\sum_{i=1}^{5} x_i = x_1 + x_2 + x_3 + x_4 + x_5 = 5 + 7 + 13 + 21 + 29 = 75$$

The mean is

$$\text{mean} = \bar{x} = \frac{\sum_{i=1}^{5} x_i}{n} = \frac{75}{5} = 15$$

When the data is presented in the form of a frequency distribution the mean is found by first multiplying each data value by its frequency. The results are added. This is equivalent to adding up all the data values. The mean is found by dividing this sum by the sum of all the frequencies. Note that the sum of the frequencies is equal to the total number of values. Consider the following example.

WORKED EXAMPLE

10.5   Thirty-eight students sit a mathematics test and their marks out of 10 are shown in Table 10.1. Find the mean mark.

Solution   Each data value, in this case the mark, is multiplied by its frequency, and the results are added. This is equivalent to adding up all the 38 individual marks. This is shown in Table 10.2.

Table 10.1
Marks of 38 students in a test

Table 10.2
Marks of 38 students multiplied by frequency

Mark, m	Frequency, f
0	0
1	0
2	1
3	0
4	1
5	7
6	16
7	8
8	3
9	1
10	1
Total	38

Mark, m	Frequency, f	$m \times f$
0	0	0
1	0	0
2	1	2
3	0	0
4	1	4
5	7	35
6	16	96
7	8	56
8	3	24
9	1	9
10	1	10
Totals	38	236

Note that the sum of all the frequencies is equal to the number of students taking the test. The number 236 is equal to the sum of all the individual marks. The mean is found by dividing this sum by the sum of all the frequencies:

$$\text{mean} = \frac{236}{38} = 6.21$$

The mean mark is 6.21 out of 10.

Using the sigma notation the formula for the mean mark of a frequency distribution with N classes, where the frequency of value x_i is f_i, becomes

Key point

$$\text{mean} = \bar{x} = \frac{\sum_{i=1}^{N} f_i \times x_i}{\sum_{i=1}^{N} f_i}$$

Note that $\sum_{i=1}^{N} f_i = n$; that is, the sum of all the frequencies equals the total number of values.

When the data is in the form of a grouped distribution the class midpoint is used to calculate the mean. Consider the following example.

WORKED EXAMPLE

10.6 The heights, to the nearest centimetre, of 100 students are given in Table 10.3. Find the mean height.

Solution Because the actual heights of students in each class are not known we use the midpoint of the class as an estimate. The midpoint of the class 164–165 is 164.5. Other midpoints and the calculation of the mean are shown in Table 10.4. Then

$$\text{mean} = \bar{x} = \frac{\sum_{i=1}^{N} f_i \times x_i}{\sum_{i=1}^{N} f_i} = \frac{17150}{100} = 171.5$$

The mean height is 171.5 cm.

Table 10.3
Heights of 100 students

Height (cm)	Frequency
164–165	4
166–167	8
168–169	10
170–171	27
172–173	30
174–175	10
176–177	6
178–179	5
Total	100

Table 10.4
Heights of 100 students with midpoints multiplied by frequency

Height (cm)	Frequency f_i	Midpoint x_i	$f_i \times x_i$
164–165	4	164.5	658.0
166–167	8	166.5	1332.0
168–169	10	168.5	1685.0
170–171	27	170.5	4603.5
172–173	30	172.5	5175.0
174–175	10	174.5	1745.0
176–177	6	176.5	1059.0
178–179	5	178.5	892.5
Total	100		17150.0

The median

A second average that also typifies a set of data is the **median**.

Key point	The **median** of a set of numbers is found by listing the numbers in ascending order and then selecting the value that lies halfway along the list.

WORKED EXAMPLE	
10.7	Find the median of the numbers
	1 2 6 7 9 11 11 11 14
Solution	The set of numbers is already given in order. The number halfway along the list is 9, because there are four numbers before it and four numbers after it in the list. Hence the median is 9.

When there is an even number of values, the median is found by taking the mean of the two middle values.

WORKED EXAMPLE	
10.8	Find the median of the following salaries: £24,000, £12,000, £16,000, £22,000, £10,000 and £25,000.
Solution	The numbers are first arranged in order as £10,000, £12,000, £16,000, £22,000, £24,000 and £25,000. Because there is an even number of values there are two middle figures: £16,000 and £22,000. The mean of these is

$$\frac{16,000 + 22,000}{2} = 19,000$$

The median salary is therefore £19,000.

The mode

A third average is the **mode**.

Key point	The **mode** of a set of values is that value that occurs most often.

WORKED EXAMPLE

10.9   Find the mode of the set of numbers

1 1 4 4 5 6 8 8 8 9

Solution   The number that occurs most often is 8, which occurs three times. Therefore 8 is the mode. Usually a mode is quoted when we want to represent the most popular value in a set.

Sometimes a set of data may have more than one mode.

WORKED EXAMPLE

10.10   Find the mode of the set of numbers

20 20 21 21 21 48 48 49 49 49

Solution   In this example there is no single value that occurs most frequently. The number 21 occurs three times, but so does the number 49. This set has two modes. The data is said to be **bimodal**.

Self-assessment questions 10.2

1. State the three different types of average commonly used in statistical calculations.

2. In an annual report, an employer of a small firm claims that the median salary for the workforce is £18,500. However, over discussions in the canteen it is apparent that no worker earns this amount. Explain how this might have arisen.

Exercise 10.2

1. Find the mean, median and mode of the following set of values: 2, 3, 5, 5, 5, 5, 8, 8, 9.

2. Find the mean of the set of numbers 1, 1, 1, 1, 1, 1, 256. Explain why the mean does not represent the data adequately. Which average might it have been more appropriate to use?

3. The marks of seven students in a test were 45%, 83%, 99%, 65%, 68%, 72% and 66%. Find the mean mark and the median mark.

4. Write out fully each of the following expressions:

(a) $\sum_{i=1}^{4} x_i$ (b) $\sum_{i=1}^{7} x_i$

(c) $\sum_{i=1}^{3} (x_i - 3)^2$ (d) $\sum_{i=1}^{4} (2 - x_i)^2$

5. Write the following concisely using sigma notation:

(a) $x_3 + x_4 + x_5 + x_6$
(b) $(x_1 - 1) + (x_2 - 1) + (x_3 - 1)$

6. Calculate the mean, median and mode of the following numbers: 1.00, 1.15, 1.25, 1.38, 1.39 and 1.40.

7. The prices of the eight executive homes advertised by a local estate agent are

   £290,000 £375,000 £325,000 £299,950

   £319,950 £327,500 £299,500 £329,500

   Find the mean price of these houses.

8. The data in the table gives the radius of 20 ball bearings. Find the class midpoints and hence calculate the average radius.

Radius (mm)	Frequency
20.56–20.58	3
20.59–20.61	6
20.62–20.64	8
20.65–20.67	3

10.3 The variance and standard deviation

Suppose we consider the test marks of two groups of three students. Suppose that the marks out of 10 for the first group are

   4   7   and   10

while those of the second group are

   7   7   and   7

It is easy to calculate the mean mark of each group: the first group has mean mark

$$\frac{4 + 7 + 10}{3} = \frac{21}{3} = 7$$

The second group has mean mark

$$\frac{7 + 7 + 7}{3} = \frac{21}{3} = 7$$

We see that both groups have the same mean mark even though the marks in the first group are widely spread, whereas the marks in the second group are all the same. If the teacher quotes just the mean mark of each group this gives no information about how widely the marks are spread. The **variance** and **standard deviation** are important and widely used statistical quantities that contain this information. Most calculators are pre-programmed to calculate these quantities. Once you understand the processes involved, check to see if your calculator can be used to find the variance and standard deviation of a set of data.

Suppose we have n values x_1, x_2, x_3 up to x_n. Their mean is $\bar{x}$ given by

$$\bar{x} = \frac{\sum_{i=1}^{n} x_i}{n}$$

The variance is found from the following formula:

$$\text{variance} = \frac{\sum_{i=1}^{n}(x_i - \bar{x})^2}{n}$$

If you study this carefully you will see that to calculate the variance we must:

- calculate the mean value $\bar{x}$
- subtract the mean from each value in turn, that is find $x_i - \bar{x}$
- square each answer to get $(x_i - \bar{x})^2$
- add up all these squared quantities to get $\sum_{i=1}^{n}(x_i - \bar{x})^2$
- divide the result by n to get

$$\frac{\sum_{i=1}^{n}(x_i - \bar{x})^2}{n}$$

which is the variance

The standard deviation is found by taking the square root of the variance:

$$\text{standard deviation} = \sqrt{\frac{\sum_{i=1}^{n}(x_i - \bar{x})^2}{n}}$$

Let us calculate the variance and standard deviation of each of the two sets of marks 4, 7, 10 and 7, 7, 7. We have already noted that the mean of each set is 7. Each stage of the calculation of the variance of the set 4, 7, 10 is shown in Table 10.5. The mean is subtracted from each number, and the results are

Table 10.5

x_i	$x_i - \bar{x}$	$(x_i - \bar{x})^2$
4	$4 - 7 = -3$	$(-3)^2 = 9$
7	$7 - 7 = 0$	$0^2 = 0$
10	$10 - 7 = 3$	$3^2 = 9$
Total		18

squared and then added. Note that when a negative number is squared the result is positive. The squares are added to give 18. In this example, the number of values equals 3. So, taking $n = 3$,

$$\text{variance} = \frac{\sum_{i=1}^{n}(x_i - \bar{x})^2}{n} = \frac{18}{3} = 6$$

The standard deviation is the square root of the variance, that is $\sqrt{6} = 2.449$. Similarly, calculation of the variance and standard deviation of the set 7, 7, 7 is shown in Table 10.6. Again, n equals 3. So

$$\text{variance} = \frac{\sum_{i=1}^{n}(x_i - \bar{x})^2}{n} = \frac{0}{3} = 0$$

Table 10.6

x_i	$x_i - \bar{x}$	$(x_i - \bar{x})^2$
7	$7 - 7 = 0$	$0^2 = 0$
7	$7 - 7 = 0$	$0^2 = 0$
7	$7 - 7 = 0$	$0^2 = 0$
Total		0

The standard deviation is the square root of the variance and so it also equals zero. The fact that the standard deviation is zero reflects that there is no spread of values. By comparison it is easy to check that the standard deviation of the set 6, 7 and 8, which also has mean 7, is equal to 0.816. The fact that the set 4, 7 and 10 has standard deviation 2.449 shows that the values are more widely spread than in the set 6, 7 and 8.

WORKED EXAMPLE

10.11   Find the variance and standard deviation of 10, 15.8, 19.2 and 8.7.

Solution   First the mean is found:

$$\bar{x} = \frac{10 + 15.8 + 19.2 + 8.7}{4} = \frac{53.7}{4} = 13.425$$

The calculation to find the variance is given in Table 10.7.

$$\text{variance} = \frac{\sum_{i=1}^{n}(x_i - \bar{x})^2}{n} = \frac{73.049}{4} = 18.262$$

The standard deviation is the square root of the variance:

$$\sqrt{18.262} = 4.273$$

Table 10.7

x_i	$x_i - \bar{x}$	$(x_i - \bar{x})^2$
10	$10 - 13.425 = -3.425$	$(-3.425)^2 = 11.731$
15.8	$15.8 - 13.425 = 2.375$	$2.375^2 = 5.641$
19.2	$19.2 - 13.425 = 5.775$	$5.775^2 = 33.351$
8.7	$8.7 - 13.425 = -4.725$	$(-4.725)^2 = 22.326$
Total		73.049

When dealing with a grouped frequency distribution with N classes the formula for the variance becomes

Key point

$$\text{variance} = \frac{\sum_{i=1}^{N} f_i (x_i - \bar{x})^2}{\sum_{i=1}^{N} f_i}$$

As before, the standard deviation is the square root of the variance.

WORKED EXAMPLE

10.12   In a period of 30 consecutive days in July the temperature in °C was recorded as follows:

18	19	20	23	24	24	21	18	17	16
16	17	17	17	18	19	20	20	22	23
24	24	25	23	21	21	20	19	19	18

(a) Produce a grouped frequency distribution showing data grouped from 16 to 17 °C, 18 to 19 °C and so on.

(b) Find the mean temperature of the grouped data.

(c) Find the standard deviation of the grouped data.

Solution   (a) The data is grouped using a tally chart as in Table 10.8.

Table 10.8

Temperature range (°C)	Tally	Frequency
16–17	$\cancel{||||}\ |$	6
18–19	$\cancel{||||}\ |||$	8
20–21	$\cancel{||||}\ ||$	7
22–23	$||||$	4
24–25	$\cancel{||||}$	5
Total		30

(b) When calculating the mean temperature from the grouped data we do not know the actual temperatures. We do know the frequency of each class. The best we can do is use the midpoint of each class as an estimate of the values in that class. The class midpoints and the calculation to determine the mean are shown in Table 10.9. The mean is then

$$\bar{x} = \frac{\sum_{i=1}^{N} f_i \times x_i}{\sum_{i=1}^{N} f_i} = \frac{603}{30} = 20.1\,°C$$

Table 10.9

Temperature range (°C)	Frequency f_i	Class midpoint x_i	$f_i \times x_i$
16–17	6	16.5	99.0
18–19	8	18.5	148.0
20–21	7	20.5	143.5
22–23	4	22.5	90.0
24–25	5	24.5	122.5
Total	30		603

(c) To find the variance and hence the standard deviation we must subtract the mean, 20.1, from each value, square and then add the results. Finally this sum is divided by 30. The complete calculation is shown in Table 10.10.

Table 10.10

Temperature range (°C)	Frequency f_i	Class midpoint x_i	$x_i - \bar{x}$	$(x_i - \bar{x})^2$	$f_i(x_i - \bar{x})^2$
16–17	6	16.5	−3.60	12.96	77.76
18–19	8	18.5	−1.60	2.56	20.48
20–21	7	20.5	0.40	0.16	1.12
22–23	4	22.5	2.40	5.76	23.04
24–25	5	24.5	4.40	19.36	96.80
Total	30				219.20

Finally the variance is given by

$$\text{variance} = \frac{\sum_{i=1}^{N} f_i(x_i - \bar{x})^2}{\sum_{i=1}^{N} f_i} = \frac{219.20}{30} = 7.307$$

The standard deviation is the square root of the variance, that is $\sqrt{7.307} = 2.703$.

Self-assessment questions 10.3

1. Why is an average often an insufficient way of describing a set of values?

2. Describe the stages involved in calculating the variance and standard deviation of a set of values $x_1, x_2, \ldots, x_n$.

Exercise 10.3

1. Find the standard deviation of each of the following sets of numbers and comment upon your answers:
    (a) 20, 20, 20, 20   (b) 16, 17, 23, 24
    (c) 0, 20, 20, 40

2. Calculate the variance and standard deviation of the following set of numbers: 1, 2, 3, 3, 3, 4, 7, 8, 9, 10.

3. The examination results of two students, Jane and Tony, are shown in the table. Find the mean and standard deviation of each of them. Comment upon the results.

	Jane	Tony
Maths	50	29
Physics	42	41
Chemistry	69	60
French	34	48
Spanish	62	80

4. The marks of 50 students in a mathematics examination are given as

45	50	62	62	68	47	45	44	48
73	62	63	62	67	80	45	41	40
23	55	21	83	67	49	48	48	62
63	79	58	71	37	32	58	54	50
62	66	68	62	81	92	62	45	49
71	72	70	49	51				

    (a) Produce a grouped frequency distribution using classes 25–29, 30–34, 35–39 and so on.
    (b) The modal class is the class with the highest frequency. State the modal class.
    (c) Calculate the mean, variance and standard deviation of the grouped frequency distribution.

Challenge Exercises 10

1. Show that
    $$\sum (x_i - \bar{x})^2 = \sum x_i^2 - n\bar{x}^2$$

2. The data set, X, comprises n items, $x_1, x_2, x_3, \ldots x_n$ with mean $\bar{x}$ and standard deviation σ_x. Each data point, x_i, is linearly transformed to produce a new data point, y_i with
    $$y_i = a + bx_i \qquad i = 1, 2, 3, \ldots, n$$

where a and b are constants.

(a) If $\bar{y}$ is the mean of the new data set show that

$$\bar{y} = a + b\bar{x}$$

(b) If σ_y is the standard deviation of the new data set show that

$$\sigma_y = b\sigma_x$$

Test and assignment exercises 10

1. Calculate the mean, median and mode of the following numbers: 2.7, 2.8, 3.1, 3.1, 3.1, 3.4, 3.8, 4.1.

2. Calculate the mean of
   (a) the first 10 whole numbers,

   $$1, 2, \ldots, 10$$

   (b) the first 12 whole numbers,

   $$1, 2, \ldots, 12$$

   (c) the first n whole numbers,

   $$1, 2, \ldots, n$$

3. A manufacturer of breakfast cereals uses two machines that pack 250 g packets of cereal automatically. In order to check the average weight, sample packets are taken and weighed to the nearest gram. The results of checking eight packets from each of the two machines are given in the table.

   Machine

1	250	250	251	257	253	250	268	259
2	249	251	250	251	252	258	254	250

   (a) Find the mean weight of each sample of eight packets.
   (b) Find the standard deviation of each sample.
   (c) Comment upon the performance of the two machines.

4. What is the median of the five numbers 18, 28, 39, 42, 43? If 50 is added as the sixth number what would the median become?

5. Express the following sums in sigma notation:
   (a) $y_1 + y_2 + y_3 + \cdots + y_7 + y_8$
   (b) $y_1^2 + y_2^2 + y_3^2 + \cdots + y_7^2 + y_8^2$
   (c) $(y_1 - \bar{y})^2 + (y_2 - \bar{y})^2 + \cdots + (y_7 - \bar{y})^2 + (y_8 - \bar{y})^2$

6. The ages of people attending a theatre performance were recorded as follows:

Age (years)	Frequency
0–9	0
10–19	6
20–29	24
30–39	42
40–49	59
50–59	53
60–69	17
70–79	8
80–89	3

(a) Calculate the mean age of the audience.

(b) Calculate the standard deviation of the distribution.

Probability

Objectives: This chapter:

- introduces theoretical and experimental probability and how to calculate them
- explains the meaning of the term 'complementary events'
- explains the meaning of the term 'independent events'

11.1 Introduction

Some events in life are impossible; other events are quite certain to happen. For example, it is impossible for a human being to live for 1000 years. We say that the probability of a human being living for 1000 years is 0. On the other hand it is quite certain that all of us will die someday. We say that the probability that all of us will die is 1. Using the letter P to stand for probability we can write

$$P(\text{a human will live for 1000 years}) = 0$$

and

$$P(\text{all of us will die someday}) = 1$$

Many other events in life are neither impossible nor certain. These have varying degrees of likelihood, or chance. For example, it is quite unlikely but not impossible that the British weather throughout a particular summer will be dominated by snowfall. It is quite likely but not certain that the life expectancy of the UK population will continue to rise in the foreseeable future. Events such as these can be assigned probabilities varying from 0 up to 1. Those having probabilities close to 1 are quite likely to happen. Those having probabilities close to 0 are almost impossible. Several events and their probabilities are shown on the

Figure 11.1
The probability scale

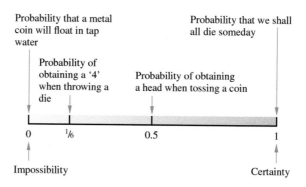

probability scale in Figure 11.1. It is important to note that no probability can lie outside the range 0 to 1.

Key point	All probabilities lie in the range [0, 1].

Complementary events

Consider the following situation. A light bulb is tested. Clearly it either works or it does not work. Here we have two events: the first is that the light bulb works and the second is that the light bulb does not work. When the bulb is tested, one or other of these events must occur. Furthermore, each event excludes the other. In such a situation we say the two events are **complementary.** In general, two events are complementary if one of them must happen and, when it does, the other event cannot. The sum of the probabilities of the two complementary events must always equal 1. This is known as **total probability.** We shall see how this result can be used to calculate probabilities shortly.

Self-assessment questions 11.1

1. All probabilities must lie in a certain range. What is this range?

2. Explain the meaning of the term 'complementary events'.

11.2 Calculating theoretical probabilities

Sometimes we have sufficient information about a set of circumstances to calculate the probability of an event occurring. For example, suppose we roll a die and ask what the probability is of obtaining a score of '5'. If the die is fair, or

unbiased, the chance of getting a '5' is the same as the chance of getting any other score. You would expect to get a '5' one time in every six. That is,

the probability of throwing a '5' is $\dfrac{1}{6}$ or 0.167

In other words there is a one in six chance of scoring a '5'. The fact that the probability is closer to 0 than to 1 means that it is quite unlikely that a '5' will be thrown, although it is not impossible. Such a probability is known as a **theoretical probability** and, when all events are equally likely, it is calculated from the following formula:

Key point

When all events are equally likely

$$P\begin{pmatrix}\text{obtaining our} \\ \text{chosen event}\end{pmatrix} = \dfrac{\text{number of ways the chosen event can occur}}{\text{total number of possibilities}}$$

For example, suppose we ask what the probability is of obtaining a score more than 4. A score more than 4 can occur in two ways, by scoring a '5' or a '6'. If the die is fair, all possible events are equally likely. The total number of possibilities is 6, therefore,

$$P(\text{score more than 4}) = \dfrac{2}{6} = \dfrac{1}{3}$$

WORKED EXAMPLES

11.1   A fair die is thrown. What is the probability of obtaining an even score?

Solution   The chosen event is throwing an even score, that is a '2', '4' or '6'. There are therefore three ways that this chosen event can occur out of a total of six, equally likely, ways. So

$$P(\text{even score}) = \dfrac{3}{6} = \dfrac{1}{2}$$

11.2   A fair coin is tossed. What is the probability that it will land with its head uppermost?

Solution   There are two equally likely ways the coin can land: head uppermost or tail uppermost. The chosen event, that the coin lands with its head uppermost, is just one of these ways. The chance of getting a head is the same as the chance of getting a tail. Therefore,

$$P(\text{head}) = \dfrac{1}{2}$$

Note from the previous example that $P(\text{tail}) = \frac{1}{2}$ and also that

$$P(\text{tail}) + P(\text{head}) = 1$$

Note that the two events, getting a head and getting a tail, are complementary because one of them must happen and either one excludes the other. Therefore the sum of the two probabilities, the total probability, equals 1.

WORKED EXAMPLE

11.3   Two coins are tossed.

(a) Write down all the possible outcomes.

(b) What is the probability of obtaining two tails?

Solution   (a) Letting H stand for head and T for tail, the possible outcomes are

$$H, H \quad H, T \quad T, H \quad T, T$$

There are four possible outcomes, each one equally likely to occur.

(b) Obtaining two tails is just one of the four possible outcomes. Therefore, the probability of obtaining two tails is $\frac{1}{4}$.

Exercise 11.2

1. A die is thrown. Find
    (a) the probability of obtaining a score less than 6
    (b) the probability of obtaining a score more than 6
    (c) the probability of obtaining an even score less than 5
    (d) the probability of obtaining an even score less than 2

2. There are four Aces in a pack of 52 playing cards. What is the probability that a card selected at random is not an Ace?

3. A drawer contains six red socks, six black socks and eight blue socks. Find the probability that a sock selected at random from the drawer is

    (a) black   (b) red   (c) red or blue

4. Two dice are thrown together and their scores are added together. By considering all the possible outcomes, find the probability that the total score will be
    (a) 12   (b) 0   (c) 1   (d) 2   (e) more than 5

5. A basket contains 87 good apples and three bad ones. What is the probability that an apple chosen at random is bad?

6. A box contains 16 red blocks, 20 blue blocks, 24 orange blocks and 10 black blocks. A block is picked at random. Calculate the probability that the block is
    (a) black   (b) orange   (c) blue
    (d) red or blue   (e) red or blue or orange
    (f) not orange

7. Three coins are tossed. By considering all possible outcomes calculate the probability of obtaining
    (a) two heads and one tail
    (b) at least two heads
    (c) no heads

11.3 Calculating experimental probabilities

In some circumstances we do not have sufficient information to calculate a theoretical probability. We know that if a coin is unbiased the probability of obtaining a head is $\frac{1}{2}$. But suppose the coin is biased so that it is more likely to land with its tail uppermost. We can experiment by tossing the coin a large number of times and counting the number of tails obtained. Suppose we toss the coin 100 times and obtain 65 tails. We can then estimate the probability of obtaining a tail as $\frac{65}{100}$ or 0.65. Such a probability is known as an **experimental probability** and is accurate only if a very large number of experiments are performed. Generally, we can calculate an experimental probability from the following formula:

Key point

$$P\left(\begin{array}{c} \text{chosen event} \\ \text{occurs} \end{array}\right) = \frac{\text{number of ways the chosen event occurs}}{\text{total number of times the experiment is repeated}}$$

WORKED EXAMPLES

11.4   A biased die is thrown 1000 times and a score of '6' is obtained on 200 occasions. If the die is now thrown again what is the probability of obtaining a score of '6'?

Solution   Using the formula for the experimental probability we find

$$P(\text{throwing a '6'}) = \frac{200}{1000} = 0.2$$

If the die were unbiased the theoretical probability of throwing a '6' would be $\frac{1}{6} = 0.167$, so the die has been biased in favour of throwing a '6'.

11.5   A manufacturer produces microwave ovens. It is known from experience that the probability that a microwave oven is of an acceptable standard is 0.92. Find the probability that an oven selected at random is not of an acceptable standard.

Solution   When an oven is tested either it is of an acceptable standard or it is not. An oven cannot be both acceptable and unacceptable. The two events, that the oven is acceptable or that the oven is unacceptable, are therefore complementary. Recall that the sum of the probabilities of complementary events is 1 and so

$$P(\text{oven is not acceptable}) = 1 - 0.92 = 0.08$$

Self-assessment questions 11.3

1. In what circumstances is it appropriate to use an experimental probability?

2. A series of experiments is performed three times. In the first of the series an experiment is carried out 100 times. In the second it is carried out 1000 times and in the third 10000 times. Which of the series of experiments is likely to lead to the best estimate of probability? Why?

Exercise 11.3

1. A new component is fitted to a washing machine. In a sample of 150 machines tested, 7 failed to function correctly. Calculate the probability that a machine fitted with the new component (a) works correctly, (b) does not work correctly.

2. In a sample containing 5000 nails manufactured by a company, 5% are too short or too long. A nail is picked at random from the production line. Estimate the probability that it is of the right length.

3. The probability that the Post Office delivers first-class mail on the following working day after posting is 0.96. If 93500 first-class letters are posted on Wednesday, how many are likely to be delivered on Thursday?

4. The probability that a car rescue service will reach a car in less than one hour is 0.87. If the rescue service is called out 17300 times in one day, calculate the number of cars reached in less than one hour.

5. Out of 50000 components tested, 48700 were found to be working well. A batch of 3000 components is delivered to a depot. How many are likely to be not working well?

11.4   Independent events

Two events are **independent** if the occurrence of either one in no way affects the occurrence of the other. For example, if an unbiased die is thrown twice the score on the second throw is in no way affected by the score on the first. The two scores are independent. The **multiplication law** for independent events states the following:

Key point

If events A and B are independent, then the probability of obtaining A and B is given by

$$P(A \text{ and } B) = P(A) \times P(B)$$

WORKED EXAMPLE

11.6   A die is thrown and a coin is tossed. What is the probability of obtaining a '6' and a head?

Solution   These events are independent since the score on the die in no way affects the result of tossing the coin, and vice versa. Therefore

$$P(\text{throwing a '6' and tossing a head}) = P(\text{throwing a '6'})$$
$$\times P(\text{tossing a head})$$
$$= \frac{1}{6} \times \frac{1}{2}$$
$$= \frac{1}{12}$$

When several events are independent of each other the multiplication law becomes

$$P(A \text{ and } B \text{ and } C \text{ and } D \ldots) = P(A) \times P(B) \times P(C) \times P(D) \ldots$$

WORKED EXAMPLE

11.7   A coin is tossed three times. What is the probability of obtaining three heads?

Solution   The three tosses are all independent events since the result of any one has no effect on the others. Therefore

$$P(3 \text{ heads}) = \frac{1}{2} \times \frac{1}{2} \times \frac{1}{2} = \frac{1}{8}$$

Self-assessment questions 11.4

1. Explain what is meant by saying two events are independent.

2. Suppose we have two packs each of 52 playing cards. A card is selected from each pack. Event A is that the card from the first pack is the Ace of Spades. Event B is that the card from the second pack is a Spade. Are these two events dependent or independent?

3. From a single pack of cards, two are removed. The first is examined. Suppose event A is that the first card is the Ace of Spades. The second card is examined. Event B is that the second card is a Spade. Are the two events dependent or independent?

Exercise 11.4

1. A die is thrown and a coin is tossed. What is the probability of getting an even score on the die and a tail?

2. Suppose you have two packs each of 52 playing cards. A card is drawn from the first and a card is drawn from the second. What is the probability that both cards are the Ace of Spades?

3. A coin is tossed eight times. What is the probability of obtaining eight tails?

4. A die is thrown four times. What is the probability of obtaining four '1's?

5. Suppose that there is an equal chance of a mother giving birth to a boy or a girl.
   (a) If one child is born find the probability that it is a boy.

   (b) If two children are born find the probability that they are both boys, assuming that the sex of neither one can influence the sex of the other.

6. The probability that a component is working well is 0.96. If four components are picked at random calculate the probability that
   (a) they all work well
   (b) none of them work well

7. The probability that a student passes a module is 0.91. If three modules are studied calculate the probability that the student passes
   (a) all three modules   (b) two modules
   (c) one module   (d) no modules

Challenge Exercise 11

1. A particular athlete knows that the probability of winning a road race is 0.23. Calculate the probability of winning:
   (a) three consecutive races
   (b) two of four races
   (c) at least one race from five

Test and assignment exercises 11

1. The following numbers are probabilities of a certain event happening. One of them is an error. Which one?

   (a) 0.5   (b) $\dfrac{3}{4}$ (c) 0.001   (d) $\dfrac{13}{4}$

2. Which of the following cannot be a probability?
   (a) 0.125   (b) −0.2   (c) 1   (d) 0

3. Events *A, B* and *C* are defined as follows. In each case state the complementary event.

   A: the lifespan of a light bulb is greater than 1000 hours
   B: it will rain on Christmas Day 2020
   C: your car will be stolen sometime in the next 100 days

4. The probability of a component manufactured in a factory being defective is 0.01. If three components are selected at random what is the probability that they all work as required?

5. A parcel delivery company guarantees 'next-day' delivery for 99% of its parcels. Out of a sample of 1800 deliveries, 15 were delivered later than the following day. Is the company living up to its promises?

6. At a certain bus stop the probability of a bus arriving late is $\frac{3}{20}$. The probability of its arriving on time is $\frac{4}{5}$. Find
   (a) the probability that the bus arrives early
   (b) the probability that the bus does not arrive late

7. Suppose you have two packs each of 52 playing cards. A card is drawn from the first and a card is drawn from the second. What is the probability that
   (a) both cards are diamonds?
   (b) both cards are black?
   (c) both cards are Kings?

8. Find the probability of obtaining an odd number when throwing a fair die once.

9. A bag contains eight red beads, four white beads and five blue beads. A bead is drawn at random. Determine the probability that it is
   (a) red   (b) white   (c) black   (d) blue   (e) red or white   (f) not blue

10. Two cards are selected from a pack of 52. Find the probability that they are both Aces if the first card is
    (a) replaced and   (b) not replaced

11. A pack contains 20 cards, numbered 1 to 20. A card is picked at random. Calculate the probability that the number on the card is
    (a) even   (b) 16 or more   (c) divisible by 3

12. Out of 42300 components, 846 were defective. How many defective components would you expect in a batch of 1500?

13. A biased die has the following probabilities:
    $$P(1) = 0.1, P(2) = 0.15, P(3) = 0.1, P(4) = 0.2, P(5) = 0.2, P(6) = 0.25$$

    The die is thrown twice. Calculate the probability that
    (a) both scores are '6's
    (b) both scores are '1's
    (c) the first score is odd and the second is even
    (d) the total score is 10

Correlation

> **Objectives:** This chapter:
>
> - explains how to explore the association between two variables using a scatter diagram.
> - explains what is meant by positive, negative and zero correlation
> - introduces the product-moment correlation coefficient
> - introduces Spearman's coefficient of rank correlation

12.1 Introduction

In the sciences, business, health studies, geography and many other fields, we are often interested in exploring relationships that may exist between two variables. For example, might it be true that, in general, taller people have greater weight than shorter people? Do cars with larger engine sizes travel fewer miles using a gallon of petrol than those with smaller engine sizes? Do business studies students who are good at statistics perform well in another aspect of their course?

The answers to some of these questions can be obtained using the statistics of **correlation**. As a first step, a graphical representation of the data is prepared using a **scatter diagram**. This is a simple method which helps us quickly draw some conclusions about the data. When a more quantitative, or rigorous, approach is needed a quantity known as the **correlation coefficient** can be calculated. This associates a number with the relationship between the variables and enables us to describe the strength of the relationship, or correlation, as perfect, strong, weak or non-existent. Under certain conditions we may be able to predict the value of one variable from knowledge of the other.

This chapter explains how to draw and interpret a scatter diagram, and how to calculate two types of correlation coefficient: the product-moment correlation coefficient and Spearman's coefficient of rank correlation.

12.2 Scatter diagrams

A simple and practical way of exploring relationships between two variables is the scatter diagram. Consider the following worked example.

WORKED EXAMPLE

12.1 In a study of food production in a developing country the total crop of wheat (in units of 10000 tonnes) was measured over a period of five summers. The summer rainfall (in cm) was also recorded. The data is provided in Table 12.1. Use a scatter diagram to explore the relationship between rainfall and wheat crop.

Table 12.1

Year	1	2	3	4	5
Wheat crop (10000 tonnes)	42	38	48	51	45
Rainfall (cm)	20	19	30	34	24

To draw a scatter diagram we think of each data pair (that is, each pair of values of rainfall and wheat crop, such as 20 and 42) as the coordinates of a point.

We choose one of the variables to be plotted on the horizontal axis and one on the vertical axis. At this stage, when we are simply exploring whether a relationship may exist, it does not matter which. In Figure 12.1 rainfall has been plotted on the horizonal axis and wheat crop on the vertical. Each point is represented by a ×.

The scatter diagram in Figure 12.1 shows that the points appear to cluster around an imaginary line which slopes upwards from left to right. There appears to be a **linear relationship** between the two variables.

Figure 12.1
Scatter diagram showing the association between rainfall and wheat crop

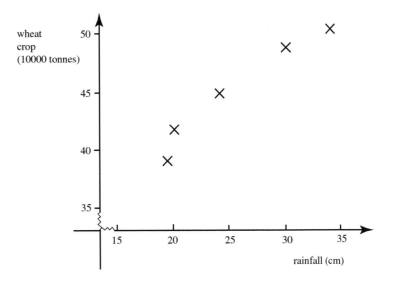

The line around which the points cluster has been drawn in by eye in Figure 12.2, although this line is not part of the scatter diagram. This line, which is closest, in some sense, to all of the data points, is called **the line of best fit**. We shall see in Chapter 13 how the equation of this line can be calculated exactly. Note that this line has a positive slope, or gradient. (You may find it useful to refresh your knowledge by re-reading.) When the points cluster closely around a line with a positive gradient we are observing **strong positive correlation** between the two variables.

The scatter diagram suggests that there is indeed a strong (linear) relationship between the two variables with low wheat crop being associated with low rainfall and high wheat crop associated with high rainfall.

Figure 12.2

The scatter diagram of Worked Example 12.1 showing the line of best fit

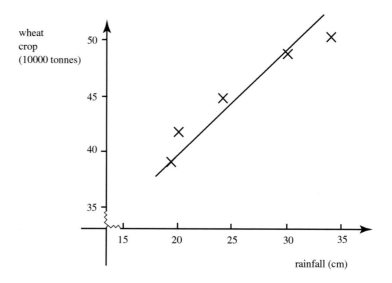

Here we illustrate how software can be used to obtain the results in Worked Example 12.1. To produce a scatter diagram and a line of best fit using Excel the data should be entered into a new Excel workbook, as shown in Figure 12.3.

The two columns of data, in this case within the range B3:C7, can then be highlighted or selected and the chart commands "scatter", "marked scatter" used to produce the required plot as shown. Various other options are available,

Figure 12.3

Excel input and output for Worked Example 12.1

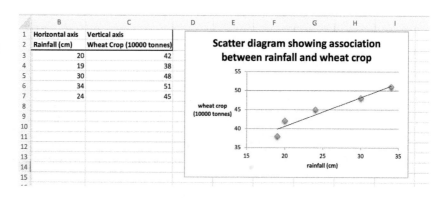

but not used here, that allow the user to join the plotted points with lines or a smooth curve and include or not include the specific points. "Chart Layout" options enable the user to insert a chart title, axis titles and scales, and to include a legend if required. Finally, by selecting the option of including a **trendline**, the line of best fit can be included. As before, we note the strong linear relationship which is apparent from the scatter diagram.

Scatter diagrams can take different forms. For example, the one in Figure 12.4(a) shows that the points cluster around a line with positive gradient but not so closely as in Figure 12.2. This is an example of weak, but positive correlation. There appears to be a relationship between the two variables but this is not as strong as in Figure 12.2.

Figure 12.4(b) shows that the points cluster closely around a line with a negative gradient. The variables here exhibit strong negative correlation. This means that high values of one variable are associated with low values of the other, and vice versa. In Figure 12.4(c) there is weak negative correlation. Finally, in Figure 12.4(d) the points do not lie on or close to a straight line at all. These points exhibit no correlation whatsoever.

When all points lie exactly on a straight line, whether with positive or negative gradient, the correlation is said to be perfect.

Key point

If X and Y are positively correlated then, on the whole, as X increases, Y increases.
If X and Y are negatively correlated then, on the whole, as X increases, Y decreases.

Figure 12.4
Scatter diagrams can illustrate different forms of association

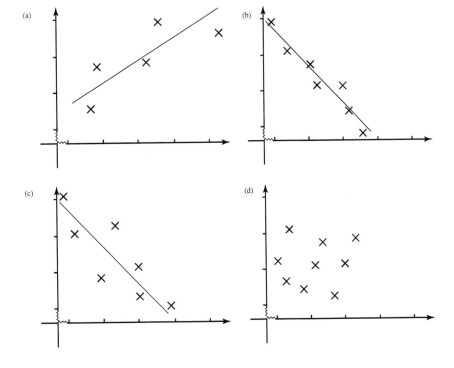

It is also possible that a relationship exists between two variables but that this relationship is not of a linear nature. For example, the scatter diagram in Figure 12.5 seems to indicate that the points lie on a well defined curve, but not on a straight line. Statistical techniques to explore non-linear relationships such as this are available but are beyond the scope of this book.

Figure 12.5
A non-linear association
between two variables

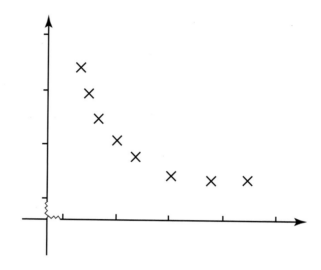

Self-assessment questions 12.2

1. Explain the purpose of a scatter diagram.

2. Explain what is meant by positive correlation, negative correlation and zero correlation.

3. Give an example of your own of two variables which might be positively correlated.

4. Give an example of your own of two variables which might be negatively correlated.

Exercise 12.2

1. For each of the following sets of data plot a scatter diagram. If possible, draw conclusions about the nature of a possible relationship between the two variables.
   (a)

X	2	8	5	4	10
Y	9	6	8	7	4

   (b)

X	50	52	54	56	58	60
Y	42	48	36	50	37	46

2. A Human Resources department in a company gathers data on the age (in years) and salary (in £1000s) of a particular group of employees. The data is given in the table below. Draw a scatter diagram for this data and comment upon the nature of the relationship between age and salary.

age	18	19	19	28	35	36	49	50	50
salary	12	13	14	18	20	21	30	38	21

12.3 Correlation coefficient

As we have seen, a scatter diagram can give us useful graphical information about the relationship between two variables. But when we require a more precise measure of a relationship, a useful quantity is the **correlation coefficient**, denoted by r. This is a number which measures the strength of the correlation. It lies between -1 and $+1$. When r takes the value 1 there is an exact straight line relationship with a positive gradient, and thus perfect positive correlation. When it takes the value -1 there is also a straight line relationship, but this time with a negative gradient. This is perfect negative correlation. When the value of r is 0 there is no correlation whatsoever. When r is close to 1 we have strong positive correlation. When r is close to -1 there is strong negative correlation.

Suppose we have gathered data in the form of n pairs of values of quantities X and Y. Suppose we denote the values of X by x_i and the values of Y by y_i where i takes values $1 \ldots n$. We can write the n pairs of values in the form (x_i, y_i). The **product-moment correlation coefficient**, r, is given by

$$r = \frac{\sum_{i=1}^{n}(x_i - \bar{x})(y_i - \bar{y})}{\sqrt{\sum_{i=1}^{n}(x_i - \bar{x})^2 \sum_{i=1}^{n}(y_i - \bar{y})^2}}$$

where $\bar{x}$ is the mean of the x values and $\bar{y}$ is the mean of the y values. In practice, when calculating the correlation coefficient by hand some regard it as easier to work with an alternative, but equivalent, version of the formula. This version avoids prior calculation of the mean values of x and y and also the differences from the mean values. It states

$$r = \frac{n\sum_{i=1}^{n}x_i y_i - \sum_{i=1}^{n}x_i \sum_{i=1}^{n}y_i}{\sqrt{n\sum_{i=1}^{n}x_i^2 - \left(\sum_{i=1}^{n}x_i\right)^2}\sqrt{n\sum_{i=1}^{n}y_i^2 - \left(\sum_{i=1}^{n}y_i\right)^2}}$$

We shall provide examples illustrating both versions.

Key point	When we have n pairs of values (x_i, y_i) of two variables X and Y, the product-moment correlation coefficient, r, is given either by

$$r = \frac{\sum\limits_{i=1}^{n} (x_i - \bar{x})(y_i - \bar{y})}{\sqrt{\sum\limits_{i=1}^{n} (x_i - \bar{x})^2 \sum\limits_{i=1}^{n} (y_i - \bar{y})^2}}$$

or, equivalently, by

$$r = \frac{n\sum\limits_{i=1}^{n} x_i y_i - \sum\limits_{i=1}^{n} x_i \sum\limits_{i=1}^{n} y_i}{\sqrt{n\sum\limits_{i=1}^{n} x_i^2 - \left(\sum\limits_{i=1}^{n} x_i\right)^2} \sqrt{n\sum\limits_{i=1}^{n} y_i^2 - \left(\sum\limits_{i=1}^{n} y_i\right)^2}}$$

If $r = 0$ there is no correlation.
If $0 < r \leqslant 1$ there is positive correlation.
If $-1 \leqslant r < 0$ there is negative correlation.
If r is close to 1 or -1 the correlation is strong.
If r is close to 0 the correlation is weak.

These formulae seem daunting, especially when first met. Work through the following example to see how to use them to calculate a correlation coefficient. In practice, once you understand what is going on you will be able to use a computer package such as Excel which has built-in commands for performing such calculations.

WORKED EXAMPLES

12.2   Four pairs of observations (x_i, y_i) of two quantities, X and Y, are listed in Table 12.2. To explore a possible relationship between the values of X and Y calculate the correlation coefficient, r, using the first of the given formulae.

Table 12.2

x_i	y_i
9	20
21	42
33	61
45	79

Solution   To calculate r it is first necessary to find the mean of the four x values, $\bar{x}$, and the mean of the four y values, $\bar{y}$. These calculations are shown in Table 12.3.

Table 12.3

x_i	y_i
9	20
21	42
33	61
45	79
108	202

$$\bar{x} = \frac{108}{4} = 27 \quad \bar{y} = \frac{202}{4} = 50.5$$

Then $\bar{x}$ is subtracted from each x value and $\bar{y}$ is subtracted from each y value, before various products are found. This information is best presented in a table, such as that in Table 12.4.

Table 12.4

x_i	y_i	$x_i - \bar{x}$	$y_i - \bar{y}$	$(x_i - \bar{x})(y_i - \bar{y})$	$(x_i - \bar{x})^2$	$(y_i - \bar{y})^2$
9	20	−18	−30.5	549	324	930.25
21	42	−6	−8.5	51	36	72.25
33	61	6	10.5	63	36	110.25
45	79	18	28.5	513	324	812.25
$\bar{x} = 27$ $\bar{y} = 50.5$		0	0	1176	720	1925

With the table complete, all the quantities required in the formula for r are available:

$$r = \frac{\sum_{i=1}^{n}(x_i - \bar{x})(y_i - \bar{y})}{\sqrt{\sum_{i=1}^{n}(x_i - \bar{x})^2 \sum_{i=1}^{n}(y_i - \bar{y})^2}} = \frac{1176}{\sqrt{(720)(1925)}} = 0.9989$$

With a value of r so close to $+1$ we conclude that there is very strong positive correlation between the variables x and y.

12.3   For the data in Worked Example 12.2 recalculate r using the second of the formulae to confirm that the result is the same.

Solution As before, we draw up a table showing the quantities required (Table 12.5):

Table 12.5

x_i	y_i	x_i^2	y_i^2	$x_i y_i$
9	20	81	400	180
21	42	441	1764	882
33	61	1089	3721	2013
45	79	2025	6241	3555
108	202	3636	12126	6630

This data can be substituted into the formula:

$$r = \frac{n \sum_{i=1}^{n} x_i y_i - \sum_{i=1}^{n} x_i \sum_{i=1}^{n} y_i}{\sqrt{n \sum_{i=1}^{n} x_i^2 - \left(\sum_{i=1}^{n} x_i \right)^2} \sqrt{n \sum_{i=1}^{n} y_i^2 - \left(\sum_{i=1}^{n} y_i \right)^2}}$$

$$= \frac{4(6630) - (108)(202)}{\sqrt{4(3636) - 108^2} \sqrt{4(12126) - 202^2}}$$

$$= \frac{4704}{\sqrt{2880} \sqrt{7700}}$$

$$= 0.9989 \quad \text{to 4 d.p.}$$

This confirms the same result is obtained using either version of the formulae.

12.4 In a recent survey of new cars, data was collected on the engine size (in cubic centimetres (cc)) and the fuel economy measured in miles per gallon (mpg). The fuel economy is calculated by simulating driving in both urban and extra-urban conditions. The data is presented in Table 12.6. Calculate the correlation coefficient for this data and comment upon the answer.

Table 12.6

x = engine size (cc)	y = economy (mpg)
999	57.6
1498	45.6
1596	37.7
1998	38.2
2295	28.8
6750	13.7

Solution   First we calculate the mean of the x and y values as shown in Table 12.7.

Table 12.7

x = engine size (cc)	y = economy (mpg)
999	57.6
1498	45.6
1596	37.7
1998	38.2
2295	28.8
6750	13.7

$$\bar{x} = \frac{15136}{6} = 2522.7 \qquad \bar{y} = \frac{221.6}{6} = 36.9$$

Then $\bar{x}$ is subtracted from each x value and $\bar{y}$ is subtracted from each y value, before various products are found. This information is best presented in a table, such as that in Table 12.8.

Table 12.8

x	y	$x_i - \bar{x}$	$y_i - \bar{y}$	$(x_i - \bar{x})(y_i - \bar{y})$	$(x_i - \bar{x})^2$	$(y_i - \bar{y})^2$
999	57.6	−1523.7	20.7	−31540.59	2321661.69	428.49
1498	45.6	−1024.7	8.7	−8914.89	1050010.09	75.69
1596	37.7	−926.7	0.8	−741.36	858772.89	0.64
1998	38.2	−524.7	1.3	−682.11	275310.09	1.69
2295	28.8	−227.7	−8.1	1844.37	51847.29	65.61
6750	13.7	4227.3	−23.2	−98073.36	17870065.29	538.24

$\bar{x} = 2522.7 \quad \bar{y} = 36.9$ −138107.94   22427667.34   1110.36

With the table complete, all the quantities required in the formula for r can be found:

$$r = \frac{\sum_{i=1}^{n}(x_i - \bar{x})(y_i - \bar{y})}{\sqrt{\sum_{i=1}^{n}(x_i - \bar{x})^2 \sum_{i=1}^{n}(y_i - \bar{y})^2}} = \frac{-138107.94}{\sqrt{(22427667.34)(1110.36)}} = -0.8752 \ (4 \text{ d.p.})$$

With a value of r so close to -1 we conclude that there is very strong negative correlation between the variables x and y. This means that, on the basis of the data supplied here, there is strong negative correlation between engine size and fuel economy. In general, smaller-sized engines in our sample are more economical than the larger engines.

You should rework this example using the second of the formulae for r.

Here we illustrate how software can be used to obtain the results in Worked Example 12.4. The columns of data in Table 12.6 should be entered into a new Excel workbook, as shown (Figure 12.6). The Excel command **CORREL (,)** can be used to calculate the required correlation coefficient by including the data ranges, B3:B8 and C3:C8 as arguments to the function.

Figure 12.6

Excel input and output for Worked Example 12.4

	D12				fx	=CORREL(B3:B8,C3:C8)
	B		C		D	E
1	x		y			
2	engine size (cc)		economy (mpg)			
3	999			57.6		
4	1498			45.6		
5	1596			37.7		
6	1998			38.2		
7	2295			28.8		
8	6759			13.7		
9						
10	typing the Excel command:					
11						
12	=CORREL(B3:B8,C3:C8)				-0.8750	
13						
14	in any selected cell calculates					
15	the required					
16	correlation coefficient, -0.8750.					
17						

As before, note the strong negative correlation between the engine size, x, and the fuel economy, y.

Self-assessment question 12.3

1. Describe in words the extent of association between two variables when (a) $r = 1$, (b) $r = -0.82$, (c) $r = -0.33$, (d) $r = 0$.

Exercise 12.3

1. Calculate the correlation coefficient r for the following data. Interpret your result.

x_i	y_i
1	11
3	51
4	96
5	115

2. Calculate the correlation coefficient r for the following data. Interpret your result.

x_i	y_i
0	2
1	5
2	8
3	11

3. Investigate the availability of computer software for the calculation of the correlation coefficient. Calculate the correlation coefficient for the data of Exercise 12.2, Question 2.

12.4 Spearman's coefficient of rank correlation

Sometimes specific values of two variables, X and Y say, are not available, but we may have data on their order, or **rank**. For example, suppose we have data on seven students, A, B, ..., F, G, which tells us who came first, second etc., in each of two athletic events – swimming and running. The data would take the form given in Table 12.9. So, for example, student A came first in both events, whereas student G came last in the swimming event and second from last in the running event.

Table 12.9

student	swimming rank	running rank
A	1	1
B	3	7
C	6	5
D	2	3
E	4	2
F	5	4
G	7	6

Suppose we want to know whether there is correlation between the two. Is there an association between good performance in the running event and good performance when swimming?

Spearman's formula can be used to calculate a **coefficient of rank correlation**, which is a number lying between -1 and 1 which provides information on the strength of the relationship exhibited by the data.

To apply the formula we need to find, for each pair of rank values, the **difference** between the ranks. So for student A, the difference between the ranks is $1 - 1 = 0$. For student G the difference is $7 - 6 = 1$. We do this for all pairs of values. Then each difference is squared. The detail is shown in Table 12.10.

Table 12.10

student	swimming rank	running rank	difference D	D^2
A	1	1	0	0
B	3	7	−4	16
C	6	5	1	1
D	2	3	−1	1
E	4	2	2	4
F	5	4	1	1
G	7	6	1	1
				24

If there are n pairs of values, the coefficient of rank correlation is given by

$$r = 1 - \frac{6\sum\limits_{i=1}^{n}D^2}{n(n^2 - 1)}$$

In this case $n = 7$ and so

$$r = 1 - \frac{6 \times 24}{7(7^2 - 1)} = 1 - \frac{144}{(7)(48)} = 0.57 \quad (2 \text{ d.p.})$$

On the basis of this data we can conclude there is a moderate positive correlation between performance in the two athletic events.

Key point

Spearman's coefficient of rank correlation: Given n pairs of values which are the rank orders of two variables X and Y, the **coefficient of rank correlation** is given by

$$r = 1 - \frac{6\sum\limits_{i=1}^{n}D^2}{n(n^2 - 1)}$$

where D is the difference between the ranks of the corresponding values of X and Y.

Here we illustrate how software can be used to obtain the Spearman coefficient of rank correlation using the data in Table 12.9. The data has been entered into a new Excel workbook, here in cells **A3:C9** as shown in Figure 12.7. In order to apply the formula

$$r = 1 - \frac{6\sum\limits_{i=1}^{n}D^2}{n(n^2 - 1)}$$

we need a column to hold the difference in each pair of ranks, D, and the squared differences, D^2. So, for example the difference in ranks for Student A is found by placing the formula **=B3-C3** in cell **D3**. This can be 'copied down' by using the mouse to position the cursor in the lower right corner of the cell until a + sign appears, and then dragging down as far as necessary. Similarly, the squared difference for Student A is placed in cell **E3** using the formula **=D3^2**, and this too can be copied down the column as before. The results are shown in Figure 12.7. These squared differences can be summed using **=SUM(E3:E9)**. We have included a cell to hold the number of pairs of data values, *n*, here equal to 7. Finally the Spearman coefficient can be calculated by inserting the formula into another cell: **=1-6*E11/(E12*(E12^2-1)**. The result is 0.57 as before, and we conclude there is moderate positive correlation between performance in the two events.

Figure 12.7
Excel input and output for calculation of Spearman's coefficient of rank correlation

E13 =1-6*E11/(E12*(E12^2-1))

	A	B	C	D	E	F
1						
2	Student	Swimming rank	Running rank	Difference	Difference Squared	
3	A	1	1	0	0	
4	B	3	7	-4	16	
5	C	6	5	1	1	
6	D	2	3	-1	1	
7	E	4	2	2	4	
8	F	5	4	1	1	
9	G	7	6	1	1	
10						
11				SUM	24	
12				N	7	
13				Spearman	0.5714	
14						

It is worth pointing out that Spearman's coefficient is the same as Pearson's product-moment correlation coefficient calculated using the ranks of the data. The result, 0.57, can be readily verified using **=CORREL(B3:B9,C3:C9)**. Clearly the use of software avoids the need for the long-winded method as used in Worked Examples 12.2 to 12.4.

Self assessment question 12.4

1. In what circumstances might you use the coefficient of rank correlation rather than the product-moment correlation coefficient?

Exercise 12.4

1. The table shows the rank order of six students in their mathematics and their science tests:

student	maths rank	science rank
A	1	1
B	3	6
C	6	5
D	2	3
E	4	2
F	5	4

Find the coefficient of rank correlation and comment upon the strength of any relationship.

2. The table shows the rank order of 10 countries in terms of the amount per capita spent upon education and the wealth of that country:

country	education spend per capita	wealth
A	4	6
B	3	4
C	6	5
D	5	7
E	7	8
F	8	9
G	10	10
H	9	1
I	1	3
J	2	2

Find the coefficient of rank correlation and comment upon the strength of any relationship.

3. Suppose you are given the rank orders of two variables and suppose that the ranks agree exactly: that is, when the rank of X is 1, the rank of Y is 1, and so on. Show that Spearman's coefficient of rank correlation, r, is 1.

Challenge Exercise 12

1. Two variables, x_i and y_i, are related by

$$y_i = mx_i + c \qquad i = 1,2,3,\ldots,n$$

where m and c are constants, that is, there is a linear relationship between x_i and y_i. Show that the product-moment correlation coefficient, r, is ± 1.

Test and assignment exercises 12

1. Calculate the correlation coefficient r for the following data. Interpret your result.

x_i	y_i
0	11
1	7
2	3

2. Figure 12.8 shows several scatter diagrams. Comment upon the nature of possible relationships between the two variables.

Figure 12.8

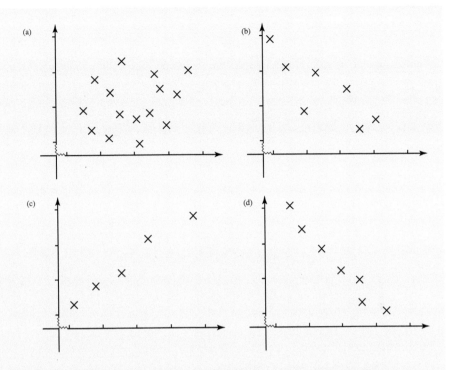

3. The table gives the mean summer temperature (in °C) at a holiday resort during the past six years together with volume (in litres) of ice cream purchased from local shops and vendors:

Year	1	2	3	4	5	6
Mean temperature (°C)	10	14	18	11	12	10
Volume (1000 litres)	20	32	33	24	23	18

Calculate the correlation coefficient for this data and comment upon any possible relationship.

4. The table provides data on seven families. It shows annual income and the amount spent in 2015 on family holidays. Rank the data and calculate Spearman's coefficient of rank correlation. Comment upon the calculated value.

family	annual income	holiday spend
A	24,000	875
B	56,000	5400
C	36,000	2100
D	29,500	400
E	100,000	1250
F	58,000	4250
G	38,000	2259

Regression

Objectives: This chapter:

- explains the concept of simple linear regression
- shows how to calculate the regression line of Y on X
- shows how to use the regression equation to predict values of the dependent variable, Y, given values of the independent variable, X

13.1 Introduction

In Chapter 12 we introduced **correlation** in order to explore the relationship between two variables, X and Y say, measured on some object of interest. We drew scatter diagrams to explore possible relationships visually and calculated the correlation coefficient, which gave us an indication of the strength of the relationship between the two variables.

In correlation, the two variables, X and Y, have equal 'status' and when a scatter diagram is drawn it does not matter which variable is plotted on the horizontal axis and which is plotted on the vertical axis. Whilst the diagrams will differ if we switch axes, the correlation coefficient will be the same either way. This is because it measures the degree of association between the two variables but does not attribute any dependency, cause or effect.

We now move on to study **regression.** The purpose of regression is to predict the value of one of the variables given a value of the other variable. When we use the data to predict the value of Y corresponding to a value of X that we choose, we refer to this as 'regression of Y on X'. So regression is subtly different from correlation. The status of the two variables is not the same since we are regarding Y as being a variable whose value depends upon the value we choose for X. In such cases we refer to X as the **independent variable** and Y as the **dependent variable.** Statistical textbooks often refer to X as the **predictor** and Y as the **response variable** because from a value of X we can *predict* the corresponding value of Y.

For example, we might be interested in trying to predict the blood pressure of a member of a group of workers given his or her age. To do this we could select several members of the group, chosen by age, X, and measure their blood pressure, Y. We then use this data to calculate the regression of blood pressure on age. This produces a regression equation which can then predict the blood pressure (without actually measuring it) of another worker given only his or her age.

In any regression analysis, values of the independent variable, X, should be preselected. For example, we may decide to select workers aged 20, 25, 30, 35, 40, . . . , 60 and measure the blood pressures, Y, of these chosen individuals. A scatter diagram is then drawn. Provided the diagram indicates that the points are scattered around an imaginary straight line then it is appropriate to calculate a **regression equation** for this line. This is the equation of the line which best fits the data and which can then be used to predict unknown values of Y.

13.2 The regression equation

Suppose we have gathered a set of data by selecting values of the variable, X, and measuring values of the corresponding variable, Y, upon each of n objects. Let the values of X be $x_1, x_2, \ldots, x_n$ and the corresponding values of Y be $y_1, y_2, \ldots, y_n$.

The regression equation is the equation of the straight line which most closely fits all of the given data. It is given in the standard form of an equation of a straight line which we shall write as

$$y = a + bx$$

So here, a is the vertical intercept of the line with the y axis, and b is the gradient of the line. The value of b is calculated first using the formula

$$b = \frac{n \sum_{i=1}^{n} x_i y_i - \left(\sum_{i=1}^{n} x_i \right)\left(\sum_{i=1}^{n} y_i \right)}{n \sum_{i=1}^{n} x_i^2 - \left(\sum_{i=1}^{n} x_i \right)^2}$$

The vertical intercept, a, is then given by

$$a = \frac{\sum_{i=1}^{n} y_i - b \sum_{i=1}^{n} x_i}{n}$$

The derivation of these formulae, which is beyond the scope of this book, relies on a technique which, loosely, makes the square of the vertical difference between each point on the scatter diagram and the line of best fit as small as possible. The proof can be found in most statistical textbooks. The formulae look very complicated when met for the first time, but in essence they require us simply to multiply some values together and add them up, as we shall see.

Key point

Given values of variables X and Y measured on n objects of interest, the regression line of Y on X is given by $y = a + bx$ where

$$b = \frac{n\sum_{i=1}^{n} x_i y_i - \left(\sum_{i=1}^{n} x_i\right)\left(\sum_{i=1}^{n} y_i\right)}{n\sum_{i=1}^{n} x_i^2 - \left(\sum_{i=1}^{n} x_i\right)^2} \qquad a = \frac{\sum_{i=1}^{n} y_i - b\sum_{i=1}^{n} x_i}{n}$$

WORKED EXAMPLE

13.1   Table 13.1 shows values of X and Y measured on five individuals.

Table 13.1

individual	x_i	y_i
A	10	28
B	20	32
C	30	38
D	40	39
E	50	48

(a) Use a scatter diagram to show that there appears to be a linear relationship between X and Y.

(b) Find the equation which represents the regression of Y on X.

(c) Plot the regression line on the scatter diagram.

(d) Use the equation to predict the value of Y when $X = 37$.

Solution   (a) The given data has been used to draw the scatter diagram in Figure 13.1. Inspection of the scatter diagram gives us some confidence that the points are scattered around an imaginary line, and so it is appropriate to try to find this line using the regression equation.

Figure 13.1
Scatter diagram for
Worked Example 13.1

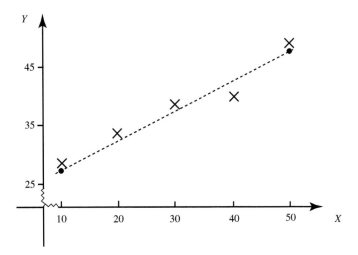

(b) Note from the formulae that we need to add up various quantities, for example

$$\sum_{i=1}^{n} x_i \quad \sum_{i=1}^{n} x_i y_i$$

In this example, in which there are five individuals, $n = 5$. It is easier to keep track of the calculations if the intermediate quantities are recorded in a table of values such as that shown in Table 13.2.

Table 13.2

individual	x_i	y_i	$x_i y_i$	x_i^2
A	10	28	280	100
B	20	32	640	400
C	30	38	1140	900
D	40	39	1560	1600
E	50	48	2400	2500

$$\sum_{i=1}^{5} x_i = 150 \quad \sum_{i=1}^{5} y_i = 185 \quad \sum_{i=1}^{5} x_i y_i = 6020 \quad \sum_{i=1}^{5} x_i^2 = 5500$$

We now have all the quantities we need to calculate b and then a:

$$b = \frac{n \sum_{i=1}^{n} x_i y_i - \left(\sum_{i=1}^{n} x_i\right)\left(\sum_{i=1}^{n} y_i\right)}{n \sum_{i=1}^{n} x_i^2 - \left(\sum_{i=1}^{n} x_i\right)^2}$$

$$= \frac{5(6020) - (150)(185)}{5(5500) - (150)^2}$$

$$= 0.47$$

Then

$$a = \frac{\sum\limits_{i=1}^{n} y_i - b \sum\limits_{i=1}^{n} x_i}{n}$$

$$= \frac{185 - (0.47)(150)}{5}$$

$$= 22.9$$

So the regression equation, $y = a + bx$, is $y = 22.9 + 0.47x$. We can use this equation to predict values of y for any values of x we choose, although it is not advisable to use it to predict values outside the interval of given values of X (that is, 10 to 50).

(c) The easiest way to draw the regression line, $y = 22.9 + 0.47x$, is to find two points which lie on the line. Note that when $x = 10$, $y = 27.6$, so the point (10, 27.6) lies on the line. When $x = 50$, $y = 22.9 + 0.47(50) = 46.4$, so the point (50, 46.4) also lies on the line. The points have been plotted and the line has been drawn in Figure 13.1.

(d) When the value of X is $x = 37$ we find $y = 22.9 + 0.47(37) = 40.29$. You could also use the straight line graph to read off the value of Y corresponding to $X = 37$ although this is not likely to be as accurate as using the equation.

   Here we illustrate how software can be used to find the line of best fit using the data in Worked Example 13.1. The columns of data in Table 13.1 should be entered into a new Excel workbook, as shown in Figure 13.2. Here the x_i values have been entered in the range E2:E6, and the y_i values in F2:F6. The Excel function LINEST can be used to calculate the slope and vertical intercept of the straight line. The two outputs can be obtained using the commands

```
=INDEX(LINEST(F2:F6,E2:E6),1)
```

to give the slope, 0.47, and

```
=INDEX(LINEST(F2:F6,E2:E6),2)
```

for the intercept, 22.9. Thus the regression equation is $y = 22.9 + 0.47x$ as before.

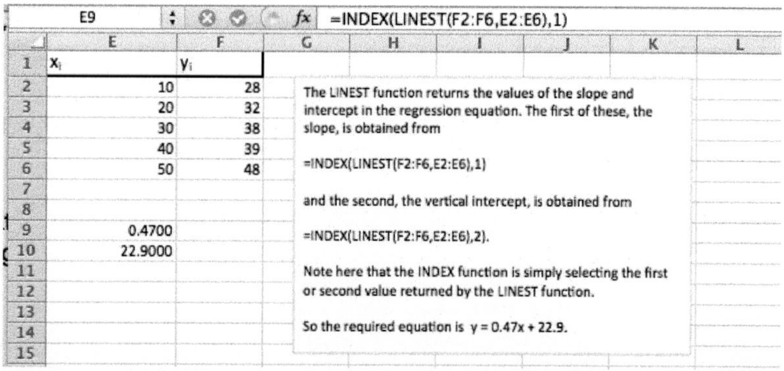

Figure 13.2
Excel input and output for Worked Example 13.1.

It is important to realise that even though we have calculated the regression equation and used it to predict a value of Y, we have no idea how good a prediction this might be. Advanced statistical techniques make it possible to state how confident we can be in our predicted value but these techniques are beyond the scope of this book.

Self-assessment questions 13.2

1. When drawing a scatter diagram for a regression problem, which variable is plotted on the horizontal axis and which on the vertical axis?

2. What is meant by the phrase 'the regression of Y on X'?

3. Explain the meaning of the terms 'predictor' and 'response variable'.

Exercise 13.2

1. Table 13.3 shows values of X and Y measured on six students.

Table 13.3

student	x_i	y_i
A	5	3
B	10	18
C	15	42
D	20	67
E	25	80
F	30	81

   (a) Use a scatter diagram to show that there appears to be a linear relationship between X and Y.
   (b) Find the equation which represents the regression of Y on X.
   (c) Plot the regression line on the scatter diagram.
   (d) Use the equation to predict the value of Y when $X = 12$.

2. It is believed that a certain drug can reduce a patient's pulse rate. In an experiment it was found that the larger the dose of the drug, the more the pulse rate reduced. A doctor wishes to find a regression equation which could be used to predict the pulse rate achieved for specific dosages. An experiment is carried out on four healthy individuals, varying the dose, X (in μg), and measuring the corresponding pulse rate, Y (in beats per minute). The data is shown in Table 13.4.

Table 13.4

individual	dose x_i	pulse rate y_i
A	2	72
B	2.5	71
C	3	65
D	3.5	60

(a) Use a scatter diagram to show that there appears to be a linear relationship between X and Y.
(b) Find the equation which represents the regression of Y on X.
(c) Plot the regression line on the scatter diagram.
(d) Use the equation to predict the pulse rate expected by administering a dose of 3.2 μg.

Test and assignment exercises 13

1. Calculate the Y on X regression line for the data in Table 13.5. Use the equation to find the value of the response variable when the predictor is 2.5.

Table 13.5

item	x_i	y_i
A	1	2.8
B	2	7.9
C	3	13.4
D	4	18.0

2. Table 13.6 shows values of Statistics Module marks, (X), and Econometrics Module marks, (Y), measured on six students.

Table 13.6

student	x_i	y_i
A	35	22
B	40	38
C	45	52
D	50	68
E	55	65
F	60	73

(a) Use a scatter diagram to show that there appears to be a linear relationship between X and Y.
(b) Find the equation which represents the regression of Y on X.
(c) Plot the regression line on the scatter diagram.
(d) Another student, G, scored 48 in her Statistics Module. What mark in Econometrics would the regression equation predict?

The Normal Distribution and Other Continuous Distributions

14

OBJECTIVES

- Compute probabilities from the normal distribution
- Use the normal distribution to solve business problems
- Use the normal probability plot to determine whether a set of data is approximately normally distributed
- Compute probabilities from the uniform distribution

▼ USING **STATISTICS**
Normal Load Times at MyTVLab

You are the vice president in charge of sales and marketing for MyTVLab, a web-based business that has evolved into a full-fledged, subscription-based streaming video service. To differentiate MyTVLab from the other companies that sell similar services, you decide to create a "Why Choose Us" web page to help educate new and prospective subscribers about all that MyTVLab offers.

As part of that page, you have produced a new video that samples the content MyTVLab streams as well as demonstrates the relative ease of setting up MyTVLab on many types of devices. You want this video to download with the page so that a visitor can jump to different segments immediately or view the video later, when offline.

You know from research (see reference 3) and past observations, Internet visitors will not tolerate waiting too long for a web page to load. One wait time measure is load time, the time in seconds that passes from first pointing a browser to a web page until the web page is fully loaded and content such as video is ready to be viewed. You have set a goal that the load time for the new sales page should rarely exceed 10 seconds (too long for visitors to wait) and, ideally, should rarely be less than 1 second (a waste of company Internet resources).

To measure this time, you point a web browser at the MyTVLab corporate test center to the new sales web page and record the load time. In your first test, you record a time of 6.67 seconds. You repeat the test and record a time of 7.52 seconds. Though consistent to your goal, you realize that two load times do not constitute strong proof of anything, especially as your assistant has performed his own test and recorded a load time of 8.83 seconds.

Could you use a method based on probability theory to ensure that most load times will be within the range you seek? MyTVLab has recorded past load times of a similar page with a similar video and determined the mean load time of that page is 7 seconds, the standard deviation of those times is 2 seconds, that approximately two-thirds of the load times are between 5 and 9 seconds, and about 95% of the load times are between 3 and 11 seconds.

Could you use these facts to assure yourself that the load time goal you have set for the new sales page is likely to be met?

n the MyTVLab scenario, you are examining the load time, a *continuous* numerical variable. You are no longer considering a table of discrete (specific) values, but a continuous range of values. For example, the phrase "load times are between 5 and 9 seconds" includes *any* value between 5 and 9 and not just the values 5, 6, 7, 8, and 9. If you plotted the phrase on a graph, you would draw a *continuous* line from 5 to 9 and not just plot five specific points.

When you add information about the shape of the range of values, such as two-thirds of the load times are between 5 and 9 seconds or about 95% of the load times are between 3 and 11 seconds, you can visualize the plot of all values as an area under a curve. If that area under the curve follows the well-known pattern of certain continuous distributions, you can use the continuous probability distribution for that pattern to estimate the likelihood that a load time is within a range of values. In the MyTVLab scenario, the past load times of a similar page describes a pattern that conforms to the pattern associated with the normal distribution, the subject of Section 14.2. That would allow you, as the vice president for sales and marketing, to use the normal distribution with the statistics given to determine if your load time goal is likely to be met.

14.1 Continuous Probability Distributions

Continuous probability distributions vary by the shape of the area under the curve. Figure 14.1 visualizes the normal, uniform, and exponential probability distributions.

FIGURE 14.1
Three continuous
probability distributions

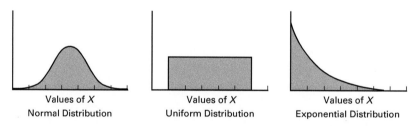

Some distributions, including the normal and uniform distributions in Figure 14.1, show a symmetrical shape. Distributions such as the right-skewed exponential distribution do not. In symmetrical distributions the mean equals the median, whereas in a right-skewed distribution the mean is greater than the median. Each of the three distributions also has unique properties.

The **normal distribution** is not only symmetrical, but bell-shaped, a shape that (loosely) suggests the profile of a bell. Being bell-shaped means that most values of the continuous variable will cluster around the mean. Although the values in a normal distribution can range from negative infinity to positive infinity, the shape of the normal distribution makes it very unlikely that extremely large or extremely small values will occur.

The **uniform distribution**, also known as the rectangular distribution, contains values that are equally distributed in the range between the smallest value and the largest value. In a uniform distribution, every value is equally likely.

The **exponential distribution** contains values from zero to positive infinity and is right-skewed, making the mean greater than the median. Its shape makes it unlikely that extremely large values will occur.

Besides visualizations such as those in Figure 14.1, a continuous probability distribution can be expressed mathematically as a *probability density function*. A **probability density function** for a specific continuous probability distribution, represented by the symbol $f(X)$, defines the distribution of the values for a continuous variable and can be used as the basis for calculations that determine the likelihood or probability that a value will be within a certain range.

14.2 The Normal Distribution

The most commonly used continuous probability distribution, the normal distribution, plays an important role in statistics and business. Because of its relationship to the Central Limit Theorem (see Section 15.2), the distribution provides the basis for classical statistical inference and can be used to approximate various discrete probability distributions. For business, many continuous variables used in decision making have distributions that closely resemble the normal distribution. The normal distribution can be used to estimate values for such variables, specifically, the probability that values occur within a specific range or interval. This probability corresponds to an area under a curve that the normal distribution defines. Because a single point on a curve, representing a specific value, cannot define an area, the area under any single point/specific value will be 0. Therefore, when using the normal distribution to estimate values of a continuous variable, the probability that the variable will be exactly a specified value is always zero.

For the MyTVLab scenario, the load time for the new sales page would be an example of a continuous variable whose distribution approximated the normal distribution. This would allow you to estimate probabilities such as the probability that the load time would be between 7 and 10 seconds, the probability that the load time would be between 8 and 9 seconds, or the probability that the load time would be between 7.99 and 8.01 seconds. You would also say properly that the probability that the load time is *exactly* 7 seconds (or any other specific value) is zero.

Exhibit 14.1 presents four important theoretical properties of the normal distribution. The distributions of many business decision-making continuous variables share all but the last of these properties which is sufficient to allow the use of the normal distribution to *estimate* the probability for specific ranges or intervals of values.

EXHIBIT 14.1

Normal Distribution Important Theoretical Properties

Symmetrical distribution. Its mean and median are equal.

Bell-shaped. Values cluster around the mean.

Interquartile range is roughly 1.33 standard deviations. Therefore, the middle 50% of the values are contained within an interval that is approximately two-thirds of a standard deviation below and two-thirds of a standard deviation above the mean.

The distribution has an infinite range ($-\infty < X < \infty$). Six standard deviations approximate this range (see page 168).

Table 14.1 presents the fill amounts, the volume of liquid placed inside a bottle, for a production run of 10,000 one-liter water bottles. Due to minor irregularities in the machinery and the water pressure, the fill amounts will vary slightly from the desired target amount, which is a bit more than 1.0 liters to prevent underfilling of bottles and the subsequent consumer unhappiness that such underfilling would cause.

TABLE 14.1
Fill Amounts for 10,000
One-liter Water Bottles

Fill Amount (liters)	Relative Frequency
< 1.025	48/10,000 = 0.0048
1.025 < 1.030	122/10,000 = 0.0122
1.030 < 1.035	325/10,000 = 0.0325
1.035 < 1.040	695/10,000 = 0.0695
1.040 < 1.045	1,198/10,000 = 0.1198
1.045 < 1.050	1,664/10,000 = 0.1664
1.050 < 1.055	1,896/10,000 = 0.1896
1.055 < 1.060	1,664/10,000 = 0.1664
1.060 < 1.065	1,198/10,000 = 0.1198
1.065 < 1.070	695/10,000 = 0.0695
1.070 < 1.075	325/10,000 = 0.0325
1.075 < 1.080	122/10,000 = 0.0122
1.080 or above	48/10,000 = 0.0048
Total	1.0000

The fill amounts for the 10,000-bottle run cluster in the interval 1.05 to 1.055 liters. The fill amounts distribute symmetrically around that grouping, forming a bell-shaped pattern which the relative frequency polygon that has been superimposed over the Figure 14.2 histogram highlights. These properties of the fill amount permit the normal distribution to be used to estimate values. Note that the distribution of fill amounts does not have an infinite range as fill amounts can never be less than 0 or more than the entire, fixed volume of a bottle. Therefore, the normal distribution can only be an approximation of the fill amount distribution, a distribution that fails to have that fourth important property of a true normal distribution.

FIGURE 14.2
Relative frequency histogram and polygon of the amount filled in 10,000 water bottles

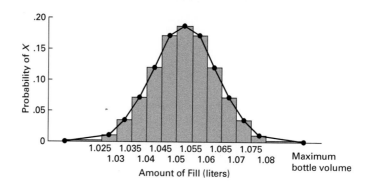

Role of the Mean and the Standard Deviation

Each combination of a mean μ and a standard deviation σ defines a separate normal distribution. Figure 14.3 shows the normal distribution for three such combinations. Distributions A and B have the same mean but have different standard deviations. Distributions A and C have the same standard deviation but have different means. Distributions B and C have different values for both the mean and standard deviation.

FIGURE 14.3
Three normal distributions

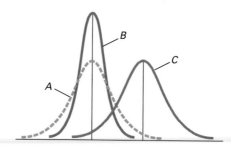

Not surprisingly, both the mean, μ, and the standard deviation, σ, appear in Equation (14.1) that defines the probability density function for the normal distribution.

NORMAL PROBABILITY DENSITY FUNCTION

$$f(X) = \frac{1}{\sqrt{2\pi\sigma}}e^{-(1/2)[(X-\mu)/\sigma]^2} \tag{14.1}$$

where

e = mathematical constant approximated by 2.71828
π = mathematical constant approximated by 3.14159
μ = mean
σ = standard deviation
X = any value of the continuous variable, where $-\infty < X < \infty$

Calculating Normal Probabilities

Examining Equation (14.1) reveals that the only terms that are not numerical constants are the mean, μ, and the standard deviation, σ. This insight allows normal probabilities to be calculated using an alternative method based in part on using the **transformation formula** that Equation (14.2) defines. Using this second method avoids the calculational complexities that the direct use of Equation (14.1) would create.

Z TRANSFORMATION FORMULA

The Z value is equal to the difference between X and the mean, μ, divided by the standard deviation, σ.

$$Z = \frac{X - \mu}{\sigma} \tag{14.2}$$

The transformation formula converts a normally distributed variable, X, to a corresponding **standardized normal variable**, Z. The formula calculates a Z value that expresses the difference of the X value from the mean, μ, in standard deviation units called *standardized units*. While a variable, X, has mean, μ, and standard deviation, σ, the standardized variable, Z, always has mean $\mu = 0$ and standard deviation $\sigma = 1$.

With a calculated Z value, the **cumulative standardized normal distribution**, to determine the probability. For example, recall from the MyTVLab scenario on page 161 that past data indicate that the sales page load time is normally distributed, with a mean $\mu = 7$ seconds and a standard deviation $\sigma = 2$ seconds. From Figure 14.4, you see that every measurement X has a corresponding standardized measurement Z, computed from Equation (14.2), the transformation formula.

FIGURE 14.4
Transformation of scales

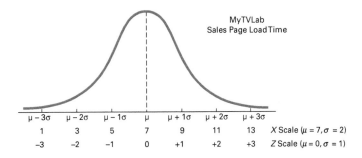

Therefore, a load time of 9 seconds is equivalent to 1 standardized unit (1 standard deviation) above the mean because

$$Z = \frac{9 - 7}{2} = +1$$

A load time of 1 second is equivalent to -3 standardized units (3 standard deviations) below the mean because

$$Z = \frac{1 - 7}{2} = -3$$

In Figure 14.4, the standard deviation is the unit of measurement. In other words, a time of 9 seconds is 2 seconds (1 standard deviation) higher, or *slower*, than the mean time of 7 seconds. Similarly, a time of 1 second is 6 seconds (3 standard deviations) lower, or *faster*, than the mean time.

To further illustrate the transformation formula, suppose that the technical support web page has a load time that is normally distributed, with a mean $\mu = 4$ seconds and a standard deviation $\sigma = 1$ second. Figure 14.5 shows this distribution.

FIGURE 14.5
A different transformation
of scales

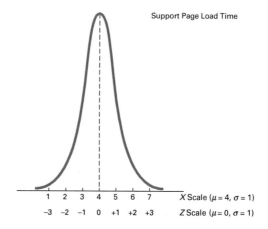

Support Page Load Time

| | X Scale ($\mu = 4$, $\sigma = 1$) |
| Z Scale ($\mu = 0$, $\sigma = 1$) |

Comparing these results with those of the sales page, you see that a load time of 5 seconds is 1 standard deviation above the mean download time because

$$Z = \frac{5 - 4}{1} = +1$$

A time of 1 second is 3 standard deviations below the mean load time because

$$Z = \frac{1 - 4}{1} = -3$$

Having determined the Z value, you use a table of values from the cumulative standardized normal distribution to look up the normal probability. Suppose you wanted to find the probability that the load time for the MyTVLab sales page is less than 9 seconds. Recall from page 165 that transforming $X = 9$ to standardized Z units, given a mean $\mu = 7$ seconds and a standard deviation $\sigma = 2$ seconds, leads to a Z value of $+1.00$.

With this value, find the cumulative area under the normal curve less than (to the left of) $Z = +1.00$. To read the probability or area under the curve less than $Z = +1.00$, you scan down the Z column until you locate the Z value of interest (in 10ths) in the Z row for 1.0. Next, you read across this row until you intersect the column that contains the 100ths place of the Z value. Therefore, in the body of the table, the probability for $Z = 1.00$ corresponds to the intersection of the row $Z = 1.0$ with the column $Z = .00$. Table 14.2, shows this intersection. The probability listed at the intersection is 0.8413, which means that there is an 84.13% chance that the download time will be less than 9 seconds. Figure 14.6 on page 167 graphically shows this probability.

student TIP

When discussing the normal or other continuous distributions, the word *area* has the same meaning as *probability*.

TABLE 14.2
Finding a Cumulative Area under the Normal Curve

Source: Extracted from Table E.2.

Cumulative Probabilities

Z	.00	.01	.02	.03	.04	.05	.06	.07	.08	.09
0.0	.5000	.5040	.5080	.5120	.5160	.5199	.5239	.5279	.5319	.5359
0.1	.5398	.5438	.5478	.5517	.5557	.5596	.5636	.5675	.5714	.5753
0.2	.5793	.5832	.5871	.5910	.5948	.5987	.6026	.6064	.6103	.6141
0.3	.6179	.6217	.6255	.6293	.6331	.6368	.6406	.6443	.6480	.6517
0.4	.6554	.6591	.6628	.6664	.6700	.6736	.6772	.6808	.6844	.6879
0.5	.6915	.6950	.6985	.7019	.7054	.7088	.7123	.7157	.7190	.7224
0.6	.7257	.7291	.7324	.7357	.7389	.7422	.7454	.7486	.7518	.7549
0.7	.7580	.7612	.7642	.7673	.7704	.7734	.7764	.7794	.7823	.7852
0.8	.7881	.7910	.7939	.7967	.7995	.8023	.8051	.8078	.8106	.8133
0.9	.8159	.8186	.8212	.8238	.8264	.8289	.8315	.8340	.8365	.8389
1.0	.8413	.8438	.8461	.8485	.8508	.8531	.8554	.8577	.8599	.8621

FIGURE 14.6
Determining the area less
than Z from a cumulative
standardized normal
distribution

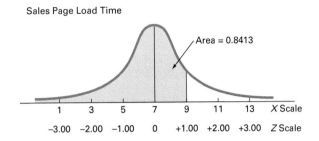

Sales Page Load Time

Area = 0.8413

| 1 | 3 | 5 | 7 | 9 | 11 | 13 | X Scale |

−3.00 −2.00 −1.00 0 +1.00 +2.00 +3.00 Z Scale

However, for the other website, you see that a time of 5 seconds is 1 standardized unit above the mean time of 4 seconds. Thus, the probability that the load time will be less than 5 seconds is also 0.8413. Figure 14.7 shows that regardless of the value of the mean, μ, and standard deviation, σ, of a normally distributed variable, Equation (14.2) can transform the X value to a Z value.

Now that you have learned to use Equation (14.2), you can answer many questions related to the sales page load time, including whether achieving the load time goal is likely, using the normal distribution.

FIGURE 14.7
Demonstrating a
transformation of scales
for corresponding
cumulative portions under
two normal curves

student TIP

You will find it very
helpful when computing
probabilities under the
normal curve if you
draw a normal curve
and then enter the
values for the mean and
X below the curve and
shade the desired area
to be determined under
the curve.

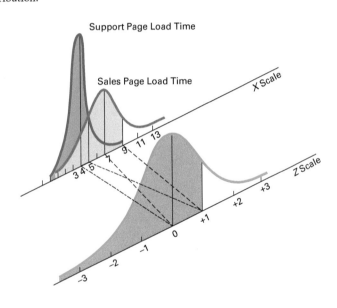

Support Page Load Time

Sales Page Load Time

X Scale

Z Scale

EXAMPLE 14.1

Finding $P(X > 9)$

What is the probability that the load time for the MyTVLab sales page will be more than 9 seconds?

SOLUTION The probability that the load time will be less than 9 seconds is 0.8413 (see Figure 14.6). Thus, the probability that the load time will be more than 9 seconds is the *complement* of less than 9 seconds, $1 - 0.8413 = 0.1587$. Figure 14.8 illustrates this result.

FIGURE 14.8
Finding $P(X > 9)$

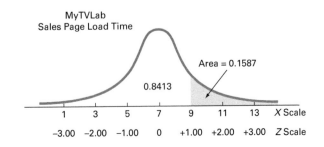

MyTVLab
Sales Page Load Time

Area = 0.1587

0.8413

| 1 | 3 | 5 | 7 | 9 | 11 | 13 | X Scale |

−3.00 −2.00 −1.00 0 +1.00 +2.00 +3.00 Z Scale

EXAMPLE 14.2

Finding $P(X < 7$ or $X > 9)$

What is the probability that the load time for the MyTVLab will be less than 7 seconds or more than 9 seconds?

SOLUTION To find this probability, you separately calculate the probability of a load time less than 7 seconds and the probability of a load time greater than 9 seconds and then add these two probabilities together. Figure 14.9 illustrates this result.

FIGURE 14.9
Finding
$P(X < 7$ or $X > 9)$

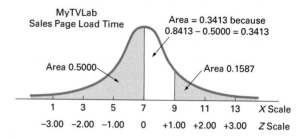

Because the mean is 7 seconds, and because the mean is equal to the median in a normal distribution, 50% of load times are under 7 seconds. From Example 14.1, you know that the probability that the load time is greater than 9 seconds is 0.1587. Therefore, the probability that a load time is under 7 or over 9 seconds, $P(X < 7$ or $X > 9)$, is $0.5000 + 0.1587 = 0.6587$.

EXAMPLE 14.3

Finding
$P(5 < X < 9)$

What is the probability that load time for the MyTVLab sales page will be between 5 and 9 seconds—that is, $P(5 < X < 9)$?

SOLUTION In Figure 14.10, you can see that the area of interest is located between two values, 5 and 9.

FIGURE 14.10
Finding $P(5 < X < 9)$

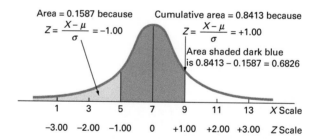

In Example 14.1 on page 167, you already found that the area under the normal curve less than 9 seconds is 0.8413. To find the area under the normal curve less than 5 seconds,

$$Z = \frac{5 - 7}{2} = -1.00$$

You look up $Z = -1.00$ and find 0.1587. Therefore, the probability that the load time will be between 5 and 9 seconds is $0.8413 - 0.1587 = 0.6826$, as displayed in Figure 14.10.

The result of Example 14.3 enables you to state that for any normal distribution, 68.26% of the values are within ± 1 standard deviation of the mean. From Figure 14.11, you can see that 95.44% of the values are within ± 2 standard deviations of the mean. Thus, 95.44% of the download times are between 3 and 11 seconds. From Figure 14.12, you can see that 99.73% of the values are within ± 3 standard deviations above or below the mean.

Thus, 99.73% of the load times are between 1 and 13 seconds. Therefore, it is unlikely (0.0027, or only 27 in 10,000) that a load time will be so fast or so slow that it will take less than 1 second or more than 13 seconds. In general, you can use 6σ (i.e., 3 standard deviations below the mean to 3 standard deviations above the mean) as a practical approximation of the range for normally distributed data.

FIGURE 14.11
Finding $P(3 < X < 11)$

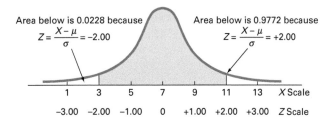

FIGURE 14.12
Finding $P(1 < X < 13)$

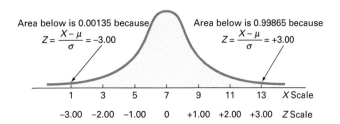

Figures 14.10, 14.11, and 14.12 illustrate that for any normal distribution,

- Approximately 68.26% of the values fall within ± 1 standard deviation of the mean
- Approximately 95.44% of the values fall within ± 2 standard deviations of the mean
- Approximately 99.73% of the values fall within ± 3 standard deviations of the mean

This result is the justification for the empirical rule. The accuracy of the empirical rule increases the closer the variable follows the normal distribution.

VISUAL EXPLORATIONS

Exploring the Normal Distribution

Open the **VE-Normal Distribution add-in workbook** to explore the normal distribution. When this workbook opens properly, it adds a Normal Distribution menu in the Add-ins tab (Apple menu in Excel for Mac).

To explore the effects of changing the mean and standard deviation on the area under a normal distribution curve, select **Normal Distribution → Probability Density Function**. The add-in displays a normal curve for the MyTVLab website download example and a floating control panel (top right). Use the control panel spinner buttons to change the values for the mean, standard deviation, and X value and then note the effects of these changes on the probability of X < value and the corresponding shaded area under the curve. To see the normal curve labeled with Z values, click **Z Values**. Click **Reset** to reset the control panel values. Click **Finish** to finish exploring.

To create shaded areas under the curve for problems similar to Examples 14.2 and 14.3, select **Normal Distribution → Areas**. In the Areas dialog box (bottom right), enter values, select an Area Option, and click **OK**. The add-in creates a normal distribution curve with areas that are shaded according to the values you entered.

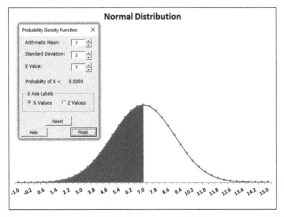

Finding X Values

The solutions to Examples 14.1 through 14.3 require finding the area under the normal curve that corresponds to a specific X value. Other problems require the opposite: Finding the X value that corresponds to a specific area. To do so, you first solve Equation (14.2) for X and use that result, Equation (14.3), to find the X value.

FINDING AN X VALUE ASSOCIATED WITH A KNOWN PROBABILITY

The X value is equal to the mean, μ, plus the product of the Z value and the standard deviation, σ.

$$X = \mu + Z\sigma \qquad\qquad (14.3)$$

To find a *particular* value associated with a known probability, follow these steps:

- Sketch the normal curve and then place the values for the mean and X on the X and Z scales.
- Find the cumulative area less than X.
- Shade the area of interest.
- Determine the Z value corresponding to the area under the normal curve less than X.
- Using Equation (14.3), solve for X: $X = \mu + Z\sigma$

Examples 14.4 and 14.5 demonstrate this technique using the five-step procedure to find a particular value associated with a known probability.

EXAMPLE 14.4

Finding the X Value
for a Cumulative
Probability of 0.10

How much time (in seconds) will elapse before the fastest 10% of the MyTVLab sales pages load time occur?

SOLUTION Because 10% of the load times are expected to occur in under X seconds, the area under the normal curve less than this value is 0.1000. You search for the area or probability of 0.1000. The closest result is 0.1003, as shown in Table 14.3.

TABLE 14.3
Finding a Z Value
Corresponding to a
Particular Cumulative
Area (0.10) under the
Normal Curve

Source: Extracted from
Table E.2.

Cumulative Probabilities

Z	.00	.01	.02	.03	.04	.05	.06	.07	.08	.09
⋮	⋮	⋮	⋮	⋮	⋮	⋮	⋮	⋮		⋮
−1.5	.0668	.0655	.0643	.0630	.0618	.0606	.0594	.0582	.0571	.0559
−1.4	.0808	.0793	.0778	.0764	.0749	.0735	.0721	.0708	.0694	.0681
−1.3	.0968	.0951	.0934	.0918	.0901	.0885	.0869	.0853	.0838	.0823
−1.2	.1151	.1131	.1112	.1093	.1075	.1056	.1038	.1020	.1003	.0985

Working from this area to the margins of the table, you find that the Z value corresponding to the particular Z row (−1.2) and Z column (.08) is −1.28 (see Figure 14.13).

FIGURE 14.13
Finding Z to
determine X

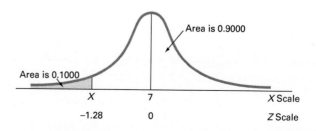

Area is 0.9000

Area is 0.1000

| | X | 7 | X Scale |
| | −1.28 | 0 | Z Scale |

▶*(continued)*

Once you find Z, you use Equation (14.3) on page 170 to determine the X value. Substituting $\mu = 7$, $\sigma = 2$, and $Z = -1.28$,

$$X = \mu + Z\sigma$$
$$X = 7 + (-1.28)(2) = 4.44 \text{ seconds}$$

Thus, 10% of the load times are 4.44 seconds or less.

EXAMPLE 14.5

Finding the *X* Values That Include 95% of the Download Times

What are the lower and upper values of X, symmetrically distributed around the mean, that include 95% of the load times for the MyTVLab sales page?

You need to find the lower value of X (called X_L). Then, you find the upper value of X (called X_U). Because 95% of the values are between X_L and X_U, and because X_L and X_U are equally distant from the mean, 2.5% of the values are below X_L (see Figure 14.14).

FIGURE 14.14
Finding *Z* to determine X_L

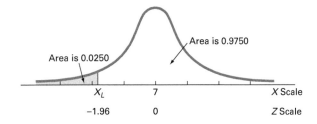

Although X_L is not known, you can find the corresponding Z value because the area under the normal curve less than this Z is 0.0250. Using the body of Table 14.4, you search for the probability 0.0250.

TABLE 14.4
Finding a *Z* Value Corresponding to a Cumulative Area of 0.025 Under the Normal Curve

Source: Extracted from Table E.2.

					Cumulative Area					
Z	.00	.01	.02	.03	.04	.05	.06	.07	.08	.09
⋮	⋮	⋮	⋮	⋮	⋮	⋮	⋮	⋮	⋮	⋮
−2.0	.0228	.0222	.0217	.0212	.0207	.0202	.0197	.0192	.0188	.0183
−1.9	.0287	.0281	.0274	.0268	.0262	.0256	.0250	.0244	.0239	.0233
−1.8	.0359	.0351	.0344	.0336	.0329	.0322	.0314	.0307	.0301	.0294

Working from the body of the table to the margins of the table, you see that the Z value corresponding to the particular Z row (-1.9) and Z column (.06) is -1.96.

Once you find Z, the final step is to use Equation (14.3) on page 171 as follows:

$$X = \mu + Z\sigma$$
$$= 7 + (-1.96)(2)$$
$$= 7 - 3.92 = 3.08 \text{ seconds}$$

You use a similar process to find X_U. Because only 2.5% of the load times take longer than X_U seconds, 97.5% of the load times take less than X_U seconds. From the symmetry of the normal distribution, you find that the desired Z value, as shown in Figure 14.15 on page 172, is $+1.96$ (because Z lies to the right of the standardized mean of 0). You can also extract this Z value from Table 14.5. You can see that 0.975 is the area under the normal curve less than the Z value of $+1.96$.

▶(*continued*)

FIGURE 14.15
Finding Z to determine X_U

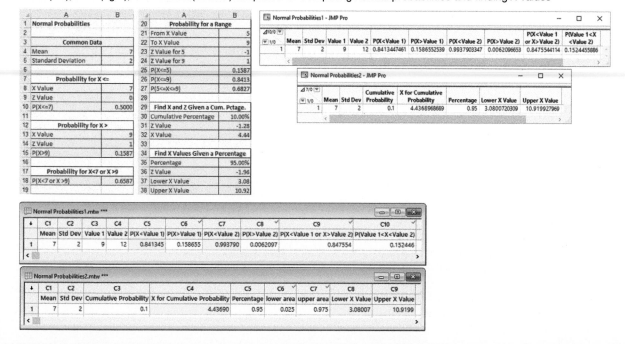

Area is 0.9750

Area is 0.0250

| | 7 | X_U | X Scale |
| | 0 | +1.96 | Z Scale |

TABLE 14.5
Finding a Z Value Corresponding to a Cumulative Area of 0.975 Under the Normal Curve

Source: Extracted from Table E.2.

					Cumulative Area					
Z	.00	.01	.02	.03	.04	.05	.06	.07	.08	.09
⋮	⋮	⋮	⋮	⋮	⋮	⋮	⋮	⋮	⋮	⋮
+1.8	.9641	.9649	.9656	.9664	.9671	.9678	.9686	.9693	.9699	.9706
+1.9	.9713	.9719	.9726	.9732	.9738	.9744	.9750	.9756	.9761	.9767
+2.0	.9772	.9778	.9783	.9788	.9793	.9798	.9803	.9808	.9812	.9817

Using Equation (14.3) on page 170,

$$X = \mu + Z\sigma$$
$$= 7 + (+1.96)(2)$$
$$= 7 + 3.92 = 10.92 \text{ seconds}$$

Therefore, 95% of the load times are between 3.08 and 10.92 seconds.

Excel, JMP, and Minitab can automate normal probability calculations. The Normal Excel Guide Workbook and the Normal JMP and Minitab projects present this functionality as a worksheet or data table template designed to help solve the various types of normal probability problems that Examples 14.1 through 14.5 illustrate. Figure 14.16 displays these templates. For Excel, the entire template consists of the COMPUTE worksheet of the Normal workbook (shown in two parts). For JMP and Minitab, the template consists of two data tables (or worksheets) named Normal Probabilities1 and Normal Probabilities2 in the Normal project.

FIGURE 14.16
Excel (left), JMP (right), and Minitab (bottom) templates for computing normal probabilities and finding X values

All three templates use formulas to compute cell values and two, the Excel and JMP templates, automatically recalculate when you enter new values for the mean, standard deviation, and, if applicable, the X value(s) and percentages. (The Minitab template is semi-automatic and the values in the tinted cells require using menu commands as the Minitab Guide for this chapter explains.) The Excel, JMP, and Minitab Guides for this chapter explain how to use the templates to solve specific Example (14.1 through 14.5) problems. The SHORT TAKES for Chapter 14 discuss the formulas that each template uses, explaining all statistical functions that those formulas use.

CONSIDER THIS

What Is Normal?

Ironically, the statistician who popularized the use of "normal" to describe the distribution discussed in Section 14.2 was someone who saw the distribution as anything but the everyday, anticipated occurrence that the adjective *normal* usually suggests.

Starting with an 1894 paper, Karl Pearson argued that measurements of phenomena do not naturally, or "normally," conform to the classic bell shape. While this principle underlies much of statistics today, Pearson's point of view was radical to contemporaries who saw the world as standardized and normal. Pearson changed minds by showing that some populations are naturally *skewed* (coining that term in passing), and he helped put to rest the notion that the normal distribution underlies all phenomena.

Today, people still make the type of mistake that Pearson refuted. As a student, you are probably familiar with discussions about grade inflation, a real phenomenon at many schools. But have you ever realized that a "proof" of this inflation—that there are "too few" low grades because grades are skewed toward A's and B's—wrongly implies that grades should be "normally" distributed? Because college students represent small *nonrandom* samples, there are plenty of reasons to suspect that the distribution of grades would not be "normal."

Misunderstandings about the normal distribution have occurred both in business and in the public sector through the years. These misunderstandings have caused a number of business blunders and have sparked several public policy debates, including the causes of the collapse of large financial institutions in 2008. According to one theory, the investment banking industry's application of the normal distribution to assess risk may have contributed to the global collapse (see "A Finer Formula for Assessing Risks," *New York Times*, May 11, 2010, p. B2 and reference 8). Using the normal distribution led these banks to overestimate the probability of having stable market conditions and underestimate the chance of unusually large market losses.

According to this theory, the use of other distributions that have less area in the middle of their curves, and, therefore, more in the "tails" that represent unusual market outcomes, may have led to less serious losses.

As you study this chapter, make sure you understand the assumptions that must hold for the proper use of the "normal" distribution, assumptions that were not explicitly verified by the investment bankers. And, most importantly, always remember that the name *normal distribution* does not mean normal in the everyday sense of the word.

PROBLEMS FOR SECTION 14.2

LEARNING THE BASICS

14.1 Given a standardized normal distribution (with a mean of 0 and a standard deviation of 1, what is the probability that
a. Z is less than 1.20?
b. Z is greater than 1.25?
c. Z is between 1.25 and 1.70?
d. Z is less than 1.20 or greater than 1.70?

14.2 Given a standardized normal distribution (with a mean of 0 and a standard deviation of 1, what is the probability that
a. Z is between -1.23 and 1.64?
b. Z is less than -1.27 or greater than 1.74?
c. For normal data with values symmetrically distributed around the mean, find the Z values that contain 95% of the data.
d. Find the value of Z such that the area to the right is 2.5% of the total area under the normal curve.

14.3 Given a standardized normal distribution (with a mean of 0 and a standard deviation of 1, what is the probability that
a. Z is less than 1.16.
b. Z is greater than -0.21.
c. Z is less than -0.21 or greater than 0.21
d. Z less than -0.21 or greater than 2.06.

14.4 Given a standardized normal distribution (with a mean of 0 and a standard deviation of 1, determine the following probabilities:
a. $P(Z < -0.37)$
b. $P(Z > 2.06)$
c. $P(-1.90 < Z < -0.21)$
d. Find the value of Z such that the area to the right of Z is 15.87%

14.5 Given a normal distribution with $\mu = 70$ and $\sigma = 20$, what is the probability that
a. $X > 110$.
b. $X < 10$.
c. $X < 70$ or $X > 130$.
d. Between what two X values (symmetrically distributed around the mean) are 70% of the values.

14.6 Given a normal distribution with $\mu = 30$ and $\sigma = 4$, what is the probability that
a. $X > 38$.
b. $X < 25$.
c. Find the X value such that the area to the left of X is 5% of the total area under the normal curve.
d. Between what two X values (symmetrically distributed around the mean) are 40% of the values?

APPLYING THE CONCEPTS

14.7 In 2015, the per capita consumption of bottled water in the United States was reported to be 36.2 gallons.
Source: Data extracted from **bottledwater.org/economics/bottled-water-market**.

Assume that the per capita consumption of bottled water in the United States is approximately normally distributed with a mean of 36.2 gallons and a standard deviation of 10 gallons.
a. What is the probability that someone in the United States consumed more than 33 gallons of bottled water in 2015?
b. What is the probability that someone in the United States consumed between 10 and 20 gallons of bottled water in 2015?
c. What is the probability that someone in the United States consumed less than 10 gallons of bottled water in 2015?
d. Ninety-nine percent of the people in the United States consumed less than how many gallons of bottled water?

✓SELF TEST **14.8** A regional airline carrier determined that the number of kilo meters travelled per airplane per year is normally distributed with a mean of 700 thousand kilo meters and a standard deviation of a 100 thousand kilo meters.
a. What percentage of the planes is expected to travel between450 and 700 thousand kilo meters in a year?
b. What proportion of the planes is expected to travel between350 and 600 thousand kilo meters in a year?
c. Find the distance in kilo meters travelled by 70% of the planes.
d. Compare the answers of parts (a) through (c) if the standard deviation is 80 thousand kilo meters.

14.9 Millennials spent an average of $103 on monthly dining in 2016.

Source: Data extracted from *Consumer Response Annual Report*, available at **bit.ly/2x4CN5w**.

Assume that the amount spent on a monthly dining is normally distributed and that the standard deviation is $12.
a. What is the probability that a randomly selected millennial spent more than $110?
b. What is the probability that a randomly selected millennial spent between $70 and $124?
c. Between what two values will the middle 95 percent of the amounts spent fall?

14.10 The scores on a university entrance exam are normally distributed with a mean of 72% and a standard deviation of 15.
a. Find the probability that a student taking the entrance exam will score below 81.

b. Find the probability that a student taking the entrance exam will score between 65 and 71.
c. Find the grade of a student such that the corresponding probability is higher than 25%.
d. If a student scored 85 on this test and his friend scored 65 on another entrance test with a mean of 55 and a standard deviation of 2. Which of the two students scored better in reference to the group?

14.11 A Nielsen study indicates that 18- to 34-year olds spend a mean of 93 minutes watching video on their smartphones per week.
Source: Data extracted from **bit.ly/2rj8GHm**.

Assume that the amount of time watching video on a smartphone per week is normally distributed and that the standard deviation is 15 minutes.
a. What is the probability that an 18- to 34-year-old spends less than 77 minutes watching video on his or her smartphone per week?
b. What is the probability that an 18- to 34-year-old spends between 77 minutes and 109 minutes watching video on his or her smartphone per week?
c. What is the probability that an 18- to 34-year-old spends more than 109 minutes watching video on his or her smartphone per week?
d. One percent of all 18- to 34-year-olds will spend less than how many minutes watching video on his or her smartphone per week?

14.12 In 2015, the per capita consumption of soft drinks in the United States was reported to be 650 eight-ounce servings.
Source: Data extracted from **fortune.com/2016/03/29/soda-sales-drop-11th-year**.

Assume that the per capita consumption of soft drinks in the United States is approximately normally distributed with a mean of 650 eight-ounce servings and a standard deviation of 100 eight-ounce servings.
a. What is the probability that someone in the United States consumed more than 750 eight-ounce servings in 2015?
b. What is the probability that someone in the United States consumed between 450 and 500 eight-ounce servings in 2015?
c. What is the probability that someone in the United States consumed less than 450 eight-ounce servings in 2015?
d. Ninety-nine percent of the people in the United States consumed less than how many servings of eight-ounce soft drinks in 2015?

14.13 The daily exchange rate for currencies fluctuates on a daily basis due to many economic conditions affecting the business cycle. The exchange rate for a twelve month period in the year 2004 between the US dollar and the Euro (EUR) shows an approximately normally distributed behavior with a mean exchange rate of 0.804 euros for every dollar and a standard deviation of0.0255. Find the following:
a. The probability that the exchange rate between the pair of currencies between 0.798 and 0.8100.
b. The probability that the exchange rate will be larger than 0.845 euros for every dollar.
c. The exchange rate such that 98% of the data falls below it.
d. If the standard deviation is changed from the stated value to 0.03, what will the answers in (a) through (c) be?

14.3 Evaluating Normality

Recall the important theoretical properties of the normal distribution that Exhibit 14.1 lists on page 163. As Section 14.2 notes, many continuous variables used in business closely follow a normal distribution. To determine whether a set of data can be approximated by the normal distribution, you either compare the characteristics of the data with the theoretical properties of the normal distribution or construct a normal probability plot.

Comparing Data Characteristics to Theoretical Properties

Many continuous variables have characteristics that approximate theoretical properties. However, other continuous variables are often neither normally distributed nor approximately normally distributed. For such variables, the descriptive characteristics of the data are inconsistent with the properties of a normal distribution. For such a variable, you can compare the observed characteristics of the variable with what you would expect to occur if the variable follows a normal distribution. To use this method:

- Construct charts and observe their appearance. For small- or moderate-sized data sets, create a stem-and-leaf display or a boxplot. For large data sets, in addition, plot a histogram or polygon.
- Compute descriptive statistics and compare these statistics with the theoretical properties of the normal distribution. Compare the mean and median. Is the interquartile range approximately 1.33 times the standard deviation? Is the range approximately 6 times the standard deviation?
- Evaluate how the values are distributed. Determine whether approximately two-thirds of the values lie between the mean and ± 1 standard deviation. Determine whether approximately four-fifths of the values lie between the mean and ± 1.28 standard deviations. Determine whether approximately 19 out of every 20 values lie between the mean and ± 2 standard deviations.

For example, you can use these techniques to determine whether the three-year return percentages in the sample of retirement funds. Table 14.6 presents the descriptive statistics and the five-number summary for the 3YrReturn variable found in Retirement Funds that contains those return percentages and Figure 14.17 uses boxplots to visualize the 3YrReturn variable.

TABLE 14.6
Descriptive Statistics and Five-Number Summary for the Three-Year Return Percentages

Descriptive Statistics		Five-Number Summary	
Mean	7.91	Minimum	−3.40
Median	8.09	First quartile	6.14
Mode	11.93	Median	8.09
Minimum	−3.40	Third quartile	9.86
Maximum	15.32	Maximum	15.32
Range	18.72		
Variance	9.10		
Standard deviation	3.02		
Coeff. of variation	38.15%		
Skewness	−0.33		
Kurtosis	0.42		
Count	479		
Standard error	0.14		

FIGURE 14.17
Excel (top), JMP (bottom left), and Minitab (bottom right) boxplots for the three-year return percentages

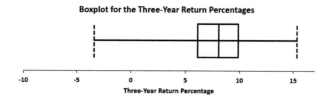

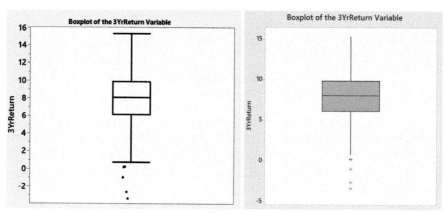

From Table 14.6, Figure 14.17, and from an ordered array of the returns (not shown), you can make the following statements about the three-year returns:

- The mean of 7.91 is slightly less than the median of 8.09. (In a normal distribution, the mean and median are equal.)
- The boxplot is slightly left-skewed. (The normal distribution is symmetrical.)
- The interquartile range of 3.72 is approximately 1.23 standard deviations. (In a normal distribution, the interquartile range is 1.33 standard deviations.)
- The range of 18.72 is equal to 6.21 standard deviations. (In a normal distribution, the range is approximately 6 standard deviations.)
- 68.75% of the returns are within ± 1 standard deviation of the mean. (In a normal distribution, 68.26% of the values lie within ± 1 standard deviation of the mean.)
- 79.38% of the returns are within ± 1.28 standard deviations of the mean. (In a normal distribution, 80% of the values lie within ± 1.28 standard deviations of the mean.)
- 94.58% of the returns are within ± 2 standard deviations of the mean. (In a normal distribution, 95.44% of the values lie within ± 2 standard deviations of the mean.)
- The skewness statistic is -0.3288 and the kurtosis statistic is 0.4189. (In a normal distribution, each of these statistics equals zero.)

Based on these statements and the criteria given on page 175, you can conclude that the three-year returns are approximately normally distributed or, at most, slightly left-skewed. The skewness is slightly negative, and the kurtosis indicates a distribution that is slightly more peaked than a normal distribution.

Constructing the Normal Probability Plot

A **normal probability plot** is a visual display that helps you evaluate whether the data are normally distributed. One common plot is called the **quantile–quantile plot**. To create this plot, you first transform each ordered value to a Z value. For example, if you have a sample of $n = 19$, the Z value for the smallest value corresponds to a cumulative area of

$$\frac{1}{n+1} = \frac{1}{19+1} = \frac{1}{20} = 0.05$$

The Z value for a cumulative area of 0.05 is -1.65. Table 14.7 illustrates the entire set of Z values for a sample of $n = 19$.

TABLE 14.7
Ordered Values and
Corresponding Z Values
for a Sample of $n = 19$

Ordered Value	Z Value	Ordered Value	Z Value	Ordered Value	Z Value
1	−1.65	8	−0.25	14	0.52
2	−1.28	9	−0.13	15	0.67
3	−1.04	10	−0.00	16	0.84
4	−0.84	11	0.13	17	1.04
5	−0.67	12	0.25	18	1.28
6	−0.52	13	0.39	19	1.65
7	−0.39				

In a quantile–quantile plot, the Z values are plotted on the X axis, and the corresponding values of the variable are plotted on the Y axis. If the data are normally distributed, the values will plot along an approximately straight line. Figure 14.18 illustrates the typical shape of the quantile–quantile normal probability plot for a left-skewed distribution (Panel A), a normal distribution (Panel B), and a right-skewed distribution (Panel C). If the data are left-skewed, the curve will rise more rapidly at first and then level off. If the data are normally distributed, the points will plot along an approximately straight line. If the data are right-skewed, the data will rise more slowly at first and then rise at a faster rate for higher values of the variable being plotted.

FIGURE 14.18
Normal probability
plots for a left-skewed
distribution, a normal
distribution, and a right-
skewed distribution

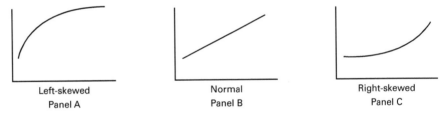

Left-skewed
Panel A

Normal
Panel B

Right-skewed
Panel C

Figure 14.19 shows Excel and JMP (quantile–quantile) normal probability plot and a Minitab normal probability plot for the three-year returns. The Excel and JMP, quantile–quantile plots show several low values followed by the bulk of the points that approximately follow a straight line except for a few low values.

FIGURE 14.19
Excel and JMP (quantile–
quantile) normal probability
plots and a Minitab normal
probability plot for the
three-year returns

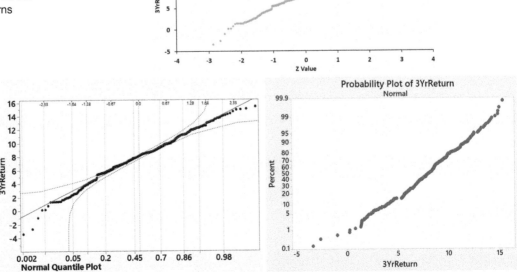

The Minitab normal probability plot has the 3YrReturn variable on the X axis and the cumulative percentage for a normal distribution on the Y axis. In this plot, if the data are normally distributed, the points will plot along an approximately straight line. In Figure 14.19, most points, other than several extreme values, approximately follow a straight line, indicating an approximately normal distribution. Had the data been right-skewed, the curve would have risen more rapidly at first and then leveled off. Had the data been left-skewed, the data would have risen more slowly at first and then risen at a faster rate for larger values of the variable.

PROBLEMS FOR SECTION 14.3

LEARNING THE BASICS

14.14 For a sample of $n = 39$ elements, find the lower and upper values of Z and show that the middle value has a Z value of zero.

14.15 For a sample of $n = 6$, list the six Z values.

APPLYING THE CONCEPTS

 14.16 The FIFA World Cup was one of the biggest sporting events of 2018. The file WC2018Players contains data of the players of the 32 teams that qualified for the event. A dummy variable is included to indicate whether a player is also a captain.

Source: Data adapted from **https://bit.ly/2zGSWRD**.

Decide whether players' ages appear to be approximately normally distributed by
a. comparing data characteristics to theoretical properties.
b. constructing a normal probability plot.

14.17 The FIFA World Cup was one of the biggest sporting events of 2018. The file WC2018TeamAge contains average age of the players (years, in 2018) of the 32 teams that qualified for the event.

Source: Data adapted from **https://bit.ly/2zGSWRD**.

Decide whether the teams' mean ages appear to be approximately normally distributed by
a. comparing data characteristics to theoretical properties.
b. constructing a normal probability plot.

14.18 Unemployment is one of the major issues most governments of the world are faced with. The file EuUnempl2017 contains employment data for 319 European regions in 2017.

Decide whether employment rates appear to be approximately normally distributed by
a. comparing data characteristics to theoretical properties.
b. constructing a normal probability plot.

14.19 Thirty companies comprise the DJIA. How big are these companies? One common method for measuring the size of a company is to use its market capitalization, which is computed by multiplying the number of stock shares by the price of a share of stock. On January 10, 2017 the market capitalization of these companies ranged from Traveler's $33.3 billion to Apple's $625.6 billion. The entire population of market capitalization values is stored in DowMarketCap.

Source: Data extracted from **money.cnn.com**, January 10, 2017.

Decide whether the market capitalization of companies in the DJIA appears to be approximately normally distributed by
a. comparing data characteristics to theoretical properties.
b. constructing a normal probability plot.
c. constructing a histogram.

14.20 One operation of a mill is to cut pieces of steel into parts that will later be used as the frame for front seats in an automotive plant. The steel is cut with a diamond saw, and the resulting parts must be within ± 0.005 inch of the length specified by the automobile company. The data come from a sample of 100 steel parts and are stored in Steel. The measurement reported is the difference, in inches, between the actual length of the steel part, as measured by a laser measurement device, and the specified length of the steel part. Determine whether the data appear to be approximately normally distributed by
a. comparing data characteristics to theoretical properties.
b. constructing a normal probability plot.

14.21 The file IndexReturn contains data about the performance of 38 indexes across the world as of July 2018.

Source: Data extracted from **https://bit.ly/2yS1QcS**.

Decide whether one-year and five-year returns appear to be approximately normally distributed by
a. comparing data characteristics to theoretical properties.
b. constructing a normal probability plot.

14.22 The file Utility contains the electricity costs, in dollars, during July of a recent year for a random sample of 50 one-bedroom apartments in a large city:

96	171	202	178	147	102	153	197	127	82
157	185	90	116	172	111	148	213	130	165
141	149	206	175	123	128	144	168	109	167
95	163	150	154	130	143	187	166	139	149
108	119	183	151	114	135	191	137	129	158

Decide whether the data appear to be approximately normally distributed by
a. comparing data characteristics to theoretical properties.
b. constructing a normal probability plot.

14.4 The Uniform Distribution

In the **uniform distribution**, the values are evenly distributed in the range between the smallest value, a, and the largest value, b. Selecting random numbers is one of the most common uses of the uniform distribution. When you use simple random sampling, you assume that each random digit comes from a uniform distribution that has a minimum value of 0 and a maximum value of 9.

Equation (14.4) defines the probability density function for the uniform distribution.

UNIFORM PROBABILITY DENSITY FUNCTION

$$f(X) = \frac{1}{b - a} \text{ if } a \leq X \leq b \text{ and 0 elsewhere} \tag{14.4}$$

where

$$a = \text{minimum value of } X$$
$$b = \text{maximum value of } X$$

Equation (14.5) defines the mean of the uniform distribution, and Equation (14.6) defines the variance and standard deviation of the uniform distribution.

MEAN OF THE UNIFORM DISTRIBUTION

$$\mu = \frac{a + b}{2} \tag{14.5}$$

VARIANCE AND STANDARD DEVIATION OF THE UNIFORM DISTRIBUTION

$$\sigma^2 = \frac{(b - a)^2}{12} \tag{14.6a}$$

$$\sigma = \sqrt{\frac{(b - a)^2}{12}} \tag{14.6b}$$

Because of its shape, the uniform distribution is sometimes called the **rectangular distribution** (see Figure 14.1 Panel B on page 162). Figure 14.20 illustrates the uniform distribution with $a = 0$ and $b = 1$. The total area inside the rectangle is 1.0, equal to the base (1.0) times the height (1.0). Having an area of 1.0 satisfies the requirement that the area under any probability density function equals 1.0.

FIGURE 14.20
Probability density function for a uniform distribution with $a = 0$ and $b = 1$

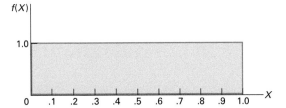

In this uniform distribution, what is the probability of getting a random number between 0.10 and 0.30? The area between 0.10 and 0.30, depicted in Figure 14.21, is equal to the base (which is $0.30 - 0.10 = 0.20$) times the height (1.0). Therefore,

$$P(0.10 < X < 0.30) = (\text{Base})(\text{Height}) = (0.20)(1.0) = 0.20$$

FIGURE 14.21
Finding $P(0.10 < X < 0.30)$
for a uniform distribution
with $a = 0$ and $b = 1$

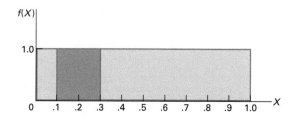

From Equations (14.5) and (14.6), the mean and standard deviation of the uniform distribution for $a = 0$ and $b = 1$ are computed as follows:

$$\mu = \frac{a + b}{2}$$

$$= \frac{0 + 1}{2} = 0.5$$

and

$$\sigma^2 = \frac{(b - a)^2}{12}$$

$$= \frac{(1 - 0)^2}{12}$$

$$= \frac{1}{12} = 0.0833$$

$$\sigma = \sqrt{0.0833} = 0.2887.$$

Thus, the mean is 0.5, and the standard deviation is 0.2887.

Example 14.6 provides another application of the uniform distribution.

EXAMPLE 14.6

Computing Uniform Probabilities

In the MyTVLab scenario on page 161, the load time of the new sales page was assumed to be normally distributed with a mean of 7 seconds. Suppose that the load time follows a uniform (instead of a normal) distribution between 4.5 and 9.5 seconds. What is the probability that a load time will take more than 9 seconds?

SOLUTION The load time is uniformly distributed from 4.5 to 9.5 seconds. The area between 9 and 9.5 seconds is equal to 0.5 seconds, and the total area in the distribution is $9.5 - 4.5 = 5$ seconds. Therefore, the probability of a load time between 9 and 9.5 seconds is the portion of the area greater than 9, which is equal to $0.5/5.0 = 0.10$. Because 9.5 is the maximum value in this distribution, the probability of a load time above 9 seconds is 0.10. In comparison, if the load time is normally distributed with a mean of 7 seconds and a standard deviation of 2 seconds (see Example 14.1 on page 167), the probability of a load time above 9 seconds is 0.1587.

PROBLEMS FOR SECTION 14.4

LEARNING THE BASICS

14.23 Suppose you select one value from a uniform distribution with $a = 0$ and $b = 10$. What is the probability that the value will be

a. between 5 and 7?
b. between 2 and 3?
c. What is the mean?
d. What is the standard deviation?

APPLYING THE CONCEPTS

✓ SELF TEST **14.24** The time it takes for a plane to be cleaned and ready for the next flight is uniformly distributed between 35 and 45 minutes. What is the probability that the cleaning time will be

a. less than 37 minutes?
b. between 35 and 40 minutes?
c. more than 38 minutes?
d. calculate the mean and the standard deviation for the cleaning time of an airplane.

14.25 A study of the time spent by visitors to finish the viewing of a marine life aquarium is uniformly distributed between 120 and 200 minutes. What is the probability that the viewing time will be
a. between 150 and 190 minutes.
b. less than 160 minutes.
c. Calculate the mean and the standard deviation for the viewing time.

14.26 How long does it take to download a two-hour HD movie from the iTunes store? According to Apple's technical support site, **support.apple.com/en-us/HT201587**, downloading such a movie using a 15 Mbit/s broadband connection should take 29–43 minutes. Assume that the download times are uniformly distributed between 29 and 43 minutes. If you download a two-hour movie, what is the probability that the download time will be

a. less than 30 minutes?
b. more than 36 minutes?
c. between 30 and 40 minutes?
d. What are the mean and standard deviation of the download times?

14.27 The scheduled time for a flight between Kuwait city and the city of Dubai in the United Arab Emirates is 75 minutes. Assume that the actual flight time is uniformly distributed between 73 and 85 minutes. Find the probability that the flight time will be
a. less than 78 minutes.
b. between 75 and 80 minutes.
c. greater than 65 minutes.
d. Calculate the mean and standard deviation of the flight time between the two cities.

14.5 The Exponential Distribution

The **exponential distribution** is a continuous distribution that is right-skewed and ranges from 0 to positive infinity (see Figure 14.1 on page 162). The **Section 14.5 online topic** discusses this distribution and illustrates its application.

14.6 The Normal Approximation to the Binomial Distribution

In many circumstances, the normal distribution can be used to approximate the binomial distribution. The **Section 14.6 online topic** discusses this technique and illustrates its use.

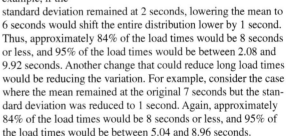

▼ USING **STATISTICS**
Normal Load Times . . . , Revisited

In the Normal Downloading at MyTVLab scenario, you were the sales and marketing vice president for a web-based business. You sought to ensure that the load time for a new sales web page would be within a certain range. By running experiments in the corporate offices, you determined that the amount of time, in seconds, that passes from first pointing a browser to a web page until the web page is fully loaded is a bell-shaped distribution with a mean load time of 7 seconds and standard deviation of 2 seconds. Using the normal distribution, you were able to calculate that approximately 84% of the load times are 9 seconds or less, and 95% of the load times are between 3.08 and 10.92 seconds.

Now that you understand how to compute probabilities from the normal distribution, you can evaluate load times of similar sales web pages that use other designs. For example, if the standard deviation remained at 2 seconds, lowering the mean to 6 seconds would shift the entire distribution lower by 1 second. Thus, approximately 84% of the load times would be 8 seconds or less, and 95% of the load times would be between 2.08 and 9.92 seconds. Another change that could reduce long load times would be reducing the variation. For example, consider the case where the mean remained at the original 7 seconds but the standard deviation was reduced to 1 second. Again, approximately 84% of the load times would be 8 seconds or less, and 95% of the load times would be between 5.04 and 8.96 seconds.

▼ SUMMARY

In this chapter, you have learned about mathematical models called probability distributions and how they can be used to solve business problems. You used discrete probability distributions in situations where the values come from a counting process such as the number of social media sites to which you belong or the number of tagged order forms in a report generated by an accounting information system. In this chapter, you learned about continuous probability distributions where the values come from a measuring process such as your height or the download time of a video.

Continuous probability distributions come in various shapes, but the most common and most important in business is the normal distribution. The normal distribution is symmetrical; thus, its mean and median are equal. It is also bell-shaped, and approximately 68.26% of its values are within ± 1 standard deviation of the mean, approximately 95.44% of its values are within ± 2 standard deviations of the mean, and approximately 99.73% of its values are within ± 3 standard deviations of the mean. Although many variables in business are closely approximated by the normal distribution, do not think that all variables can be approximated by the normal distribution.

In Section 14.3, you learned about various methods for evaluating normality in order to determine whether the normal distribution is a reasonable mathematical model to use in specific situations. In Section 14.4, you learned about another continuous distribution, the uniform distribution, that was not normal. Chapter 15 uses the normal distribution to develop the subject of statistical inference.

▼ REFERENCES

1. Gunter, B. "Q-Q Plots." *Quality Progress* (February 1994): 81–86.
2. Hogg, R. V., J. T. McKean, and A. V. Craig. *Introduction to Mathematical Statistics*, 7th ed. New York: Pearson Education, 2013.
3. Kishnan, S. and R. Sitaraman. "Video stream quality impacts viewer behavior: inferring causality using quasi-experimental designs," in *Proceedings of the 2012 ACM conference on Internet measurement conference*: 211–224. New York: ACM.
4. Levine, D. M., P. Ramsey, and R. Smidt. *Applied Statistics for Engineers and Scientists Using Microsoft Excel and Minitab.* Upper Saddle River, NJ: Prentice Hall, 2001.
5. Miller, J. "Earliest Known Uses of Some of the Words of Mathematics." **jeff560.tripod.com/mathword.html**.
6. Pearl, R. "Karl Pearson, 1857–1936." *Journal of the American Statistical Association*, 31 (1936): 653–664.
7. Pearson, E. S. "Some Incidents in the Early History of Biometry and Statistics, 1890–94." *Biometrika* 52 (1965): 3–18.
8. Taleb, N. *The Black Swan*, 2nd ed. New York: Random House, 2010.
9. Walker, H. "The Contributions of Karl Pearson." *Journal of the American Statistical Association* 53 (1958): 11–22.

▼ KEY EQUATIONS

Normal Probability Density Function

$$f(X) = \frac{1}{\sqrt{2\pi}\sigma}e^{-(1/2)[(X-\mu)/\sigma]^2} \tag{14.1}$$

Z Transformation Formula

$$Z = \frac{X-\mu}{\sigma} \tag{14.2}$$

Finding an X Value Associated with a Known Probability

$$X = \mu + Z\sigma \tag{14.3}$$

Uniform Probability Density Function

$$f(X) = \frac{1}{b-a} \tag{14.4}$$

Mean of the Uniform Distribution

$$\mu = \frac{a+b}{2} \tag{14.5}$$

Variance and Standard Deviation of the Uniform Distribution

$$\sigma^2 = \frac{(b-a)^2}{12} \tag{14.6a}$$

$$\sigma = \sqrt{\frac{(b-a)^2}{12}} \tag{14.6b}$$

KEY TERMS

cumulative standardized normal distribution
exponential distribution
normal distribution
normal probability plot
probability density function
probability density function for the normal distribution
quantile–quantile plot
rectangular distribution
standardized normal variable
transformation formula
uniform distribution

CHECKING YOUR UNDERSTANDING

14.28 How do you find the area between two values under the normal curve?

14.29 How do you find the X value that corresponds to a given percentile of the normal distribution?

14.30 What are some of the distinguishing properties of a normal distribution?

14.31 How does the shape of the normal distribution differ from the shapes of the uniform and exponential distributions?

14.32 How can you use the normal probability plot to evaluate whether a set of data is normally distributed?

▼CHAPTER REVIEW PROBLEMS

14.33 An industrial sewing machine uses ball bearings that are targeted to have a diameter of 0.75 inch. The lower and upper specification limits under which the ball bearings can operate are 0.74 inch and 0.76 inch, respectively. Past experience has indicated that the actual diameter of the ball bearings is approximately normally distributed, with a mean of 0.753 inch and a standard deviation of 0.004 inch. What is the probability that a ball bearing is
a. between the target and the actual mean?
b. between the lower specification limit and the target?
c. above the upper specification limit?
d. below the lower specification limit?
e. Of all the ball bearings, 93% of the diameters are greater than what value?

14.34 The fill amount in 2-liter soft drink bottles is normally distributed, with a mean of 2.0 liters and a standard deviation of 0.05 liter. If bottles contain less than 95% of the listed net content (1.90 liters, in this case), the manufacturer may be subject to penalty by the state office of consumer affairs. Bottles that have a net content above 2.10 liters may cause excess spillage upon opening. What proportion of the bottles will contain
a. between 1.90 and 2.0 liters?
b. between 1.90 and 2.10 liters?
c. below 1.90 liters or above 2.10 liters?
d. At least how much soft drink is contained in 99% of the bottles?
e. Ninety-nine percent of the bottles contain an amount that is between which two values (symmetrically distributed) around the mean?

14.35 In an effort to reduce the number of bottles that contain less than 1.90 liters, the bottler in Problem 14.34 sets the filling machine so that the mean is 2.02 liters. Under these circumstances, what are your answers in Problem 14.34 (a) through (e)?

14.36 *Webrooming*, researching products online before buying them in store, has become the new norm for some consumers and contrasts with *showrooming*, researching products in a physical store before purchasing online. A recent study by Interactions reported that most shoppers have a specific spending limit in place while shopping online. Findings indicate that men spend an average of $250 online before they decide to visit a store.

Source: Data extracted from **bit.ly/1JEcmqh**.

Assume that the spending limit is normally distributed and that the standard deviation is $20.
a. What is the probability that a male spent less than $210 online before deciding to visit a store?

b. What is the probability that a male spent between $270 and $300 online before deciding to visit a store?
c. Ninety percent of the amounts spent online by a male before deciding to visit a store are less than what value?
d. Eighty percent of the amounts spent online by a male before deciding to visit a store are between what two values symmetrically distributed around the mean?

Suppose that the spending limit follows a uniform distribution between $200 and $300.

e. What is the probability that a male spent less than $210 online before deciding to visit a store?
f. What is the probability that a male spent between $270 and $300 online before deciding to visit a store?
g. Compare the results of (a) and (b) to those of (e) and (f).

14.37 The file RateBeerTop50 contains the percentage alcohol, alcohol by volume (abv), number of ratings (count), rank, and average score as of July 2018 for the top 50 beers of the world. Determine whether number of ratings, alcohol by volume and average scores appear to be approximately normally distributed. Support your decisions through the use of appropriate statistics and graphs.

Source: Data extracted from **https://bit.ly/2BcTBMo**.

14.38 The evening manager of a restaurant was very concerned about the length of time some customers were waiting in line to be seated. She also had some concern about the seating times—that is, the length of time between when a customer is seated and the time he or she leaves the restaurant. Over the course of one week, 100 customers (no more than 1 per party) were randomly selected, and their waiting and seating times (in minutes) were recorded in Wait.
a. Think about your favorite restaurant. Do you think waiting times more closely resemble a uniform, an exponential, or a normal distribution?
b. Again, think about your favorite restaurant. Do you think seating times more closely resemble a uniform, an exponential, or a normal distribution?
c. Construct a histogram and a normal probability plot of the waiting times. Do you think these waiting times more closely resemble a uniform, an exponential, or a normal distribution?
d. Construct a histogram and a normal probability plot of the seating times. Do you think these seating times more closely resemble a uniform, an exponential, or a normal distribution?

14.39 The major stock market indexes had strong results in 2016. The mean one-year return for stocks in the S&P 500, a group of 500 very large companies, was +9.54%. The mean one-year return for the NASDAQ, a group of 3,200 small and medium-sized companies, was +7.50%. Historically, the one-year returns are approximately normally distributed, the standard deviation in the S&P 500 is approximately 20%, and the standard deviation in the NASDAQ is approximately 30%.

a. What is the probability that a stock in the S&P 500 gained value in 2016?

b. What is the probability that a stock in the S&P 500 gained 10% or more in 2016?

c. What is the probability that a stock in the S&P 500 lost 20% or more in 2016?

d. What is the probability that a stock in the S&P 500 lost 30% or more in 2016?

e. Repeat (a) through (d) for a stock in the NASDAQ.

f. Write a short summary on your findings. Be sure to include a discussion of the risks associated with a large standard deviation.

14.40 Interns report that when deciding on where to work, career growth, salary and compensation, location and commute, and company culture and values are important factors to them. According to reports by interns to Glassdoor, the mean monthly pay of interns at Intel is $5,940.

Source: Data extracted from **www.glassdoor.com/index.htm**.

Suppose that the intern monthly pay is normally distributed, with a standard deviation of $400. What is the probability that the monthly pay of an intern at Intel is

a. less than $5,900?

b. between $5,700 and $6,100?

c. above $6,500?

d. Ninety-nine percent of the intern monthly pays are higher than what value?

e. Ninety-five percent of the intern monthly pays are between what two values, symmetrically distributed around the mean?

14.41 According to the same Glassdoor source mentioned in Problem 14.40, the mean monthly pay for interns at Facebook is $6,589. Suppose that the intern monthly pay is normally distributed, with a standard deviation of $500. What is the probability that the monthly pay of an intern at Facebook is

a. less than $5,900?

b. between $5,700 and $6,100?

c. above $6,500?

d. Ninety-nine percent of the intern monthly pays are higher than what value?

e. Ninety-five percent of the intern monthly pays are between what two values, symmetrically distributed around the mean?

f. Compare the results for the Intel interns computed in Problem 14.40 to those of the Facebook interns.

14.42 (Class Project) One theory about the daily changes in the closing price of a stock is that these changes follow a *random walk*—that is, these daily events are independent of each other and move upward or downward in a random manner—and can be approximated by a normal distribution. To test this theory, use either a newspaper or the Internet to select one company traded on the NYSE, one company traded on the American Stock Exchange, and one company traded on the NASDAQ and then do the following:

1. Record the daily closing stock price of each of these companies for six consecutive weeks (so that you have 30 values per company).

2. Compute the daily changes in the closing stock price of each of these companies for six consecutive weeks (so that you have 30 values per company).

Note: The random-walk theory pertains to the daily changes in the closing stock price, not the daily closing stock price.

For each of your six data sets, decide whether the data are approximately normally distributed by

a. constructing the stem-and-leaf display, histogram or polygon, and boxplot.

b. comparing data characteristics to theoretical properties.

c. constructing a normal probability plot.

d. Discuss the results of (a) through (c). What can you say about your three stocks with respect to daily closing prices and daily changes in closing prices? Which, if any, of the data sets are approximately normally distributed?

CHAPTER

▼CASES

14

Managing Ashland MultiComm Services

The AMS technical services department has embarked on a quality improvement effort. Its first project relates to maintaining the target upload speed for its Internet service subscribers. Upload speeds are measured on a standard scale in which the target value is 1.0. Data collected over the past year indicate that the upload speed is approximately normally distributed, with a mean of 1.005 and a standard deviation of 0.10. Each day, one upload speed is measured. The upload speed is considered acceptable if the measurement on the standard scale is between 0.95 and 1.05.

1. Assuming that the distribution of upload speed has not changed from what it was in the past year, what is the probability that the upload speed is
   a. less than 1.0?
   b. between 0.95 and 1.0?
   c. between 1.0 and 1.05?
   d. less than 0.95 or greater than 1.05?

2. The objective of the operations team is to reduce the probability that the upload speed is below 1.0. Should the team focus on process improvement that increases the mean upload speed to 1.05 or on process improvement that reduces the standard deviation of the upload speed to 0.075? Explain.

CardioGood Fitness

Return to the CardioGood Fitness case (stored in CardioGood Fitness).

1. For each CardioGood Fitness treadmill product line, determine whether the age, income, usage, and the number of miles the customer expects to walk/run each week can be approximated by the normal distribution.
2. Write a report to be presented to the management of CardioGood Fitness detailing your findings.

More Descriptive Choices Follow-up

Follow up the More Descriptive Choices Revisited Using Statistics scenario by constructing normal probability plots for the 1-year return percentages, 5-year return percentages, and 10-year return percentages for the sample of 479 retirement funds stored in Retirement Funds . In your analysis, examine differences between the growth and value funds as well as the differences among the small, mid-cap, and large market cap funds.

Clear Mountain State Student Survey

The Student News Service at Clear Mountain State University (CMSU) has decided to gather data about the undergraduate students who attend CMSU. They create and distribute a survey of 14 questions and receive responses from 111 undergraduates (stored in StudentSurvey). For each numerical variable in the survey, decide whether the variable is approximately normally distributed by

a. comparing data characteristics to theoretical properties.
b. constructing a normal probability plot.
c. writing a report summarizing your conclusions.

Digital Case

Apply your knowledge about the normal distribution in this Digital Case, which extends the Using Statistics scenario from this chapter.

To satisfy concerns of potential customers, the management of MyTVLab has undertaken a research project to learn how much time it takes users to load a complex video features page. The research team has collected data and has made some claims based on the assertion that the data follow a normal distribution.

Open **MTL_QRTStudy.pdf**, which documents the work of a quality response team at MyTVLab. Read the internal report that documents the work of the team and their conclusions. Then answer the following:

1. Can the collected data be approximated by the normal distribution?
2. Review and evaluate the conclusions made by the MyTVLab research team. Which conclusions are correct? Which ones are incorrect?
3. If MyTVLab could improve the mean time by 5 seconds, how would the probabilities change?

EG14.2 The NORMAL DISTRIBUTION

Key Technique Use the **NORM.DIST(***X value, mean, standard deviation*, **True**) function to compute normal probabilities and use the **NORM.S.INV(***percentage*) function and the STANDARDIZE function to compute the Z value.

Example Compute the normal probabilities for Examples 14.1 through 14.3 on pages 167 and 168 and the X and Z values for Examples 14.4 and 14.5 on pages 170 and 171.

PHStat Use **Normal**.

For the example, select **PHStat→Probability & Prob. Distributions→Normal**. In this procedure's dialog box (shown below):

1. Enter **7** as the **Mean** and **2** as the **Standard Deviation**.
2. Check **Probability for: X <=** and enter **7** in its box.
3. Check **Probability for: X >** and enter **9** in its box.
4. Check **Probability for range** and enter **5** in the first box and **9** in the second box.
5. Check **X for Cumulative Percentage** and enter **10** in its box.
6. Check **X Values for Percentage** and enter **95** in its box.
7. Enter a **Title** and click **OK**.

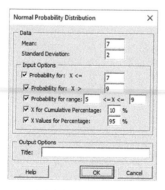

Workbook Use the **COMPUTE worksheet** of the **Normal workbook** as a template.
The worksheet already contains the data for solving the problems in Examples 14.1 through 14.5. For other problems, change the values for the **Mean**, **Standard Deviation**, **X Value**, **From X Value**, **To X Value**, **Cumulative Percentage**, and/or **Percentage**.

Unlike most other Excel Guide COMPUTE worksheets, this worksheet uses formulas in column A to dynamically

create labels based on the data values you enter. These formulas make extensive use of the ampersand operator (&) to construct the actual label. For example, the cell A10 formula **="P(X<="&B8&")"** results in the display of P(X<=7) because the initial contents of cell B8, 7, is combined with "*P(X<=*" and ")". Changing the value in cell B8 to 9, changes the label in cell A10 to P(X<=9).

EG14.3 EVALUATING NORMALITY

Constructing the Normal Probability Plot

Key Technique Use an Excel Scatter (X, Y) chart with Z values computed using the NORM.S.INV function.

Example Construct the Figure 14.19 normal probability plot for three-year return percentages for the sample of 479 retirement funds that is shown on page 177.

PHStat Use **Normal Probability Plot**.

For the example, open to the **DATA worksheet** of the **Retirement Funds workbook**. Select **PHStat→Probability & Prob. Distributions→Normal Probability Plot**. In the procedure's dialog box (shown below):

1. Enter **K1:K480** as the **Variable Cell Range**.
2. Check **First cell contains label**.
3. Enter a **Title** and click **OK**.

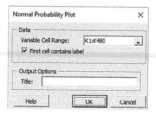

In addition to the chart sheet containing the normal probability plot, the procedure creates a plot data worksheet identical to the PlotData worksheet discussed in the *Worksheet Excel* instructions.

Workbook Use the worksheets of the **NPP workbook** as templates.
The **NormalPlot chart sheet** displays a normal probability plot using the rank, the proportion, the Z value, and the variable found in the **PLOT_DATA worksheet**. The

PLOT_DATA worksheet already contains the three-year return percentages for the example.

To construct a plot for a different variable, paste the *sorted* values for that variable in **column D** of the **PLOT_DATA worksheet**. Adjust the number of ranks in **column A** and the divisor in the formulas in **column B** to compute cumulative percentages to reflect the quantity $n + 1$ (480 for the example). (Column C formulas use the NORM.S.INV function to compute the Z values for those cumulative percentages.)

If you have fewer than 479 values, delete rows from the bottom up. If you have more than 479 values, select row 480, right-click, click **Insert** in the shortcut menu, and copy down the formulas in columns B and C to the new rows. To create your own normal probability plot for the 3YrReturn variable, open to the PLOT_DATA worksheet and select the cell range **C1:D480**. Then select **Insert→Scatter (X, Y) or Bubble Chart icon** and select the **Scatter** gallery item. Excel for Mac labels the same icon as **X Y (Scatter)**. (The icon to select is labeled as *#5* in the Charts Group Reference.)

Relocate the chart to a chart sheet, turn off the chart legend and gridlines, add axis titles, and modify the chart title.

CHAPTER 14

▼JMP GUIDE

JG14.2 The NORMAL DISTRIBUTION

Use the **Normal project worksheet templates**.

For example, to compute the normal probability for Example 14.1 on page 167, open to the **Normal Probabilities1 data table**:

1. Enter **7** in the row 1 cell of the **Mean column**.
2. Enter **2** in the row 1 cell of the **Std Dev column**.
3. Enter **9** in the row 1 cell of the **Value 1 column**.

JMP computes the probability for $P(X > 9)$ in the row 1 cell of the P(X>Value 1) column. The Normal Probabilities1 worksheet can also solve problems that are similar to Examples 14.2 and 14.3. For problems of that type, enter the second comparison value in the Value 2 column and note the computed probabilities that appear in the P(X<Value 1 or X>Value 2) column or the P(Value 1<X <Value 2) column.

Finding *X* Values

To solve problems of the type that Examples 14.4 and 14.5 on pages 170 and 171 represent, requires using the Normal Probabilities2 data table in the Normal project. For example, to find the *X* value for a cumulative probability of 0.10 (Example 14.4), open to the **Normal Probabilities2 data table** and:

1. Enter **7** in the row 1 cell of the **Mean column**.
2. Enter **2** in the row 1 cell of the **Std Dev column**.
3. Enter **0.1** in the row 1 cell of the **Cumulative Probability column**.

JMP computes the X value for the cumulative probability in the row 1 cell of the X for Cumulative Probability column. For problems similar to Example 14.5, enter the mean and standard deviation and then enter the percentage value in the Percentage column. Note the values that JMP computes in the Lower X Value and Upper X Value columns.

JG14.3 EVALUATING NORMALITY

Constructing the Normal Probability Plot

Use **Distribution**.

For example, to construct the Figure 14.19 normal probability plot for the three-year return percentages for the sample of 479 retirement funds that is shown on page 177, open to the **Retirement Funds data table**. Select **Analyze → Distribution**. In that procedure's dialog box:

1. Click **3YrReturn** in the Select Columns list and then click **Y, Columns** to add 3YrReturn to the Y, Columns box.
2. Click **OK**.

The quartiles and the five-number summary appear as part of the Quantiles report in the new Distribution window that JMP displays. In the Distribution results window:

3. Click the **3YrReturn red triangle** and select **Normal Quantile Plot** from its menu.

JMP revises the Summary Statistics report to include the normal probability plot.

▼MINITAB GUIDE

MG14.2   The NORMAL DISTRIBUTION

Use the **Normal project worksheet templates** *and* **Normal**.

For example, to compute the normal probability for Example 14.1 on page 167, open to the **Normal Probabilities1 worksheet**.

1. Enter **7** in the row 1 cell of the **Mean column** (C1).
2. Enter **2** in the row 1 cell of the **Std Dev column** (C2).
3. Enter **9** in the row 1 cell of the **Value 1 column** (C3).
4. Select **Calc → Probability Distributions → Normal**.

In the Normal Distribution dialog box (shown below):

5. Click **Cumulative probability**.
6. Enter **7** in the **Mean** box.
7. Enter **2** in the **Standard deviation** box.
8. Click **Input column** and enter **C3** in its box and press **Tab**.
9. Enter **C5** in the first **Optional storage** box.
10. Click **OK**.

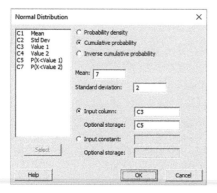

Minitab places the value 0.841345 in the row 1 cell of the P(X<Value 1) column (C5). With that value inserted, the formula in the P(>Value 1) column (C6) computes the $P(X > 9)$ solution. The Normal Probabilities1 worksheet can also solve problems that are similar to Examples 14.2 and 14.3 on page 168. For problems of that type, enter the second comparison value in the Value 2 column (C4), follow steps 1 through 10, changing the values for the mean, standard deviation, and Value 1 as necessary. Then select **Calc → Probability Distributions → Normal** and in the Normal Distribution dialog box:

1. Click **Cumulative probability**.
2. Enter the proper values in the **Mean** and **Standard deviation** boxes.

3. Click **Input column** and enter **C4** in its box and press **Tab**.
4. Enter **C7** in the first **Optional storage** box.
5. Click **OK**.

Finding *X* Values

To solve problems of the type that Examples 14.4 and 14.5 on pages 170 and 171 represent, requires using the Normal Probabilities2 worksheet in the Normal project. For example, to find the *X* value for a cumulative probability of 0.10 (Example 14.4), open to the **Normal Probabilities2 worksheet** and:

1. Enter **7** as the **Mean**, **2** as the **Std Dev**, and **0.1** as the **Cumulative Probability** in the row 1 cells of columns C1 through C3.
2. Select **Calc → Probability Distributions → Normal**.

In the Normal Distribution dialog box:

3. Click **Inverse cumulative probability**.
4. Enter **7** in the **Mean** box and **2** in the **Standard deviation** box.
5. Click **Input column** and enter **C3** in its box and press **Tab**.
6. Enter **C4** in the first **Optional storage** box.
7. Click **OK**.

Minitab places the *X* value 4.43690 in the row 1 cell of the X for Cumulative Probability column (C4). That value is the solution to the problem.

For problems similar to Example 14.5, enter the percentage value in the Percentage column (C5) and use steps 2 through 7, but enter **C6** as the **Input column** in step 5 and enter **C8** as the **Optional storage** in step 6 (to compute the Lower X Value). Then repeat steps 2 through 7, entering **C7** as the **Input column** and **C9** as the **Optional storage** column (to compute the Upper X Value).

MG14.3   EVALUATING NORMALITY

Constructing the Normal Probability Plot

Use **Probability Plot**.

For example, to construct the normal probability plot for the three-year return percentage for the sample of 479 retirement funds shown in Figure 14.19 on page 177, open to the

Retirement Funds worksheet. Select **Graph → Probability Plot** and:

1. In the Probability Plots dialog box, click **Single** and then click **OK**.

In the Probability Plot: Single dialog box (shown below):

2. Double-click **C11 3YrReturn** in the variables list to add **'3YrReturn'** to the **Graph variables** box.
3. Click **Distribution**.

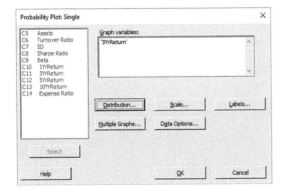

In the Probability Plot: Distribution dialog box (shown below):

4. Click the **Distribution** tab and select **Normal** from the **Distribution** drop-down list.

5. Click the **Data Display** tab. Click **Symbols only**. If the **Show confidence interval** check box is not disabled (as shown below), clear this check box.
6. Click **OK**.

7. Back in the Probability Plot: Single dialog box, click **Scale**.
8. Click the **Gridlines** tab. Clear all check boxes and then click **OK**.
9. Back in the Probability Plot: Single dialog box, click **OK**.

15

Sampling Distributions

OBJECTIVES

- Learn about the concept of the sampling distribution
- Compute probabilities related to the sample mean and the sample proportion
- Understand the importance of the Central Limit Theorem

▼USING **STATISTICS**
Sampling Oxford Cereals

As the cereal lines manager for Oxford Cereals Plant #3, you are part of the project team overseeing the installation of three new fill production lines. By automating the bag formation, fill, bag sealing, and weighing operations, three identical lines running at Plant #1 have increased the production of boxes of flaked cereals at that plant by 20% and similar gains are expected at Plant #3. In the future, these lines will give Oxford Cereals management greater production flexibility by allowing the option to use packaging other than the standard pillow bags long used.

For now, you must verify the calibration of the Plant #3 fill production machines. Proper calibration should ensure that filled boxes will contain a mean of 368 grams of cereal, among other attributes. If the calibration is imperfect, the mean weight of the boxes could vary too much from the 368 grams claimed on the preprinted boxes used in the lines. You decide to take samples of the cereal boxes being produced in the initial runs of the new lines. For each sample of cereal boxes you select, you plan to weigh each box in the sample and then calculate a sample mean. You need to determine the probability that such a sample mean could have been randomly selected from a population whose mean is 368 grams. Based on your analysis, you will have to decide whether to maintain, alter, or shut down the cereal-filling process.

n Chapter 14, you used the normal distribution to study the distribution of load times for a MyTVLab web page. In this chapter, you need to make a decision about a cereal-filling process, based on the weights of a sample of cereal boxes packaged at Oxford Cereals. You will learn about sampling distributions and how to use them to solve business problems.

15.1 Sampling Distributions

In many applications, you want to make inferences that are based on statistics calculated from samples to estimate the values of population parameters. In the next two sections, you will learn about how the sample mean (a statistic) is used to estimate the population mean (a parameter) and how the sample proportion (a statistic) is used to estimate the population proportion (a parameter). Your main concern when making a statistical inference is reaching conclusions about a population, *not* about a sample. For example, a political pollster is interested in the sample results only as a way of estimating the actual proportion of the votes that each candidate will receive from the population of voters. Likewise, as plant operations manager for Oxford Cereals, you are only interested in using the mean weight calculated from a sample of cereal boxes to estimate the mean weight of a population of boxes.

In practice, you select a single random sample of a predetermined size from the population. Hypothetically, to use the sample statistic to estimate the population parameter, you could examine *every* possible sample of a given size that could occur. A **sampling distribution** is the distribution of the results if you actually selected all possible samples. The single result you obtain in practice is just one of the results in the sampling distribution.

15.2 Sampling Distribution of the Mean

Several measures of central tendency, including the mean, median, and mode, were discussed. For several reasons, the mean is the most widely used measure of central tendency, and the sample mean is often used to estimate the population mean. The **sampling distribution of the mean** is the distribution of all possible sample means if you select all possible samples of a given size.

The Unbiased Property of the Sample Mean

learnMORE

Learn more about the unbiased property of the sample in the Short Takes for Chapter 15.

The sample mean is **unbiased** because the mean of all the possible sample means (of a given sample size, n) is equal to the population mean, μ. A simple example concerning a population of four administrative assistants demonstrates this property. Each assistant is asked to apply the same set of updates to a human resources database. Table 15.1 presents the number of errors made by each of the administrative assistants. This population distribution is shown in Figure 15.1.

TABLE 15.1
Number of Errors Made by Each of Four Administrative Assistants

Administrative Assistant	Number of Errors
Ann	$X_1 = 3$
Bob	$X_2 = 2$
Carla	$X_3 = 1$
Dave	$X_4 = 4$

FIGURE 15.1
Number of errors made by a population of four administrative assistants

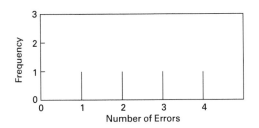

When you have data from a population, you compute the population mean by using Equation (15.1), and you compute the population standard deviation, σ, by using Equation (15.2).

POPULATION MEAN

$$\mu = \frac{\sum_{i=1}^{N} X_i}{N}$$

(15.1)

POPULATION STANDARD DEVIATION

$$\sigma = \sqrt{\frac{\sum_{i=1}^{N} (X_i - \mu)^2}{N}}$$

(15.2)

For the data of Table 15.1,

$$\mu = \frac{3 + 2 + 1 + 4}{4} = 2.5 \text{ errors}$$

and

$$\sigma = \sqrt{\frac{(3 - 2.5)^2 + (2 - 2.5)^2 + (1 - 2.5)^2 + (4 - 2.5)^2}{4}} = 1.12 \text{ errors}$$

If you select samples of two administrative assistants *with* replacement from this population, there are 16 possible samples ($N^n = 4^2 = 16$). Table 15.2 lists the 16 possible sample outcomes. If you average all 16 of these sample means, the mean of these values is equal to 2.5, which is also the mean of the population, μ.

TABLE 15.2
All 16 Samples of $n = 2$ Administrative Assistants from a Population of $N = 4$ Administrative Assistants When Sampling with Replacement

Sample	Administrative Assistants	Sample Outcomes	Sample Mean
1	Ann, Ann	3, 3	$\bar{X}_1 = 3$
2	Ann, Bob	3, 2	$\bar{X}_2 = 2.5$
3	Ann, Carla	3, 1	$\bar{X}_3 = 2$
4	Ann, Dave	3, 4	$\bar{X}_4 = 3.5$
5	Bob, Ann	2, 3	$\bar{X}_5 = 2.5$
6	Bob, Bob	2, 2	$\bar{X}_6 = 2$
7	Bob, Carla	2, 1	$\bar{X}_7 = 1.5$
8	Bob, Dave	2, 4	$\bar{X}_8 = 3$
9	Carla, Ann	1, 3	$\bar{X}_9 = 2$
10	Carla, Bob	1, 2	$\bar{X}_{10} = 1.5$
11	Carla, Carla	1, 1	$\bar{X}_{11} = 1$
12	Carla, Dave	1, 4	$\bar{X}_{12} = 2.5$
13	Dave, Ann	4, 3	$\bar{X}_{13} = 3.5$
14	Dave, Bob	4, 2	$\bar{X}_{14} = 3$
15	Dave, Carla	4, 1	$\bar{X}_{15} = 2.5$
16	Dave, Dave	4, 4	$\bar{X}_{16} = 4$
			$\mu_{\bar{X}} = 2.5$

Because the mean of the 16 sample means is equal to the population mean, the sample mean is an unbiased estimator of the population mean. Therefore, although you do not know how close the sample mean of any particular sample selected is to the population mean, you are assured that the mean of all the possible sample means that could have been selected is equal to the population mean.

Standard Error of the Mean

Figure 15.2 illustrates the variation in the sample means when selecting all 16 possible samples.

FIGURE 15.2
Sampling distribution
of the mean, based on
all possible samples
containing two
administrative assistants

Source: Data are from Table 15.2.

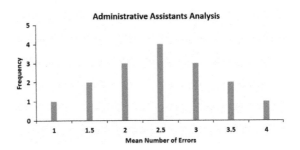

In this small example, although the sample means vary from sample to sample, depending on which two administrative assistants are selected, the sample means do not vary as much as the individual values in the population. That the sample means are less variable than the individual values in the population follows directly from the fact that each sample mean averages together all the values in the sample. A population consists of individual outcomes that can take on a wide range of values, from extremely small to extremely large. However, if a sample contains an extreme value, although this value will have an effect on the sample mean, the effect is reduced because the value is averaged with all the other values in the sample. As the sample size increases, the effect of a single extreme value becomes smaller because it is averaged with more values.

student TIP

Remember, the standard
error of the mean
measures variation
among the means not the
individual values.

The value of the standard deviation of all possible sample means, called the **standard error of the mean**, expresses how the sample means vary from sample to sample. As the sample size increases, the standard error of the mean decreases by a factor equal to the square root of the sample size. Equation (15.3) defines the standard error of the mean when sampling *with* replacement or sampling *without* replacement from large or infinite populations.

STANDARD ERROR OF THE MEAN

The standard error of the mean, $\sigma_{\bar{X}}$, is equal to the standard deviation in the population, σ, divided by the square root of the sample size, n.

$$\sigma_{\bar{X}} = \frac{\sigma}{\sqrt{n}}$$

(15.3)

Example 15.1 computes the standard error of the mean when the sample selected without replacement contains less than 5% of the entire population.

EXAMPLE 15.1

Computing the
Standard Error
of the Mean

▶(*continued*)

Returning to the cereal-filling process described in the Using Statistics scenario on page 190, if you randomly select a sample of 25 boxes without replacement from the thousands of boxes filled during a shift, the sample contains a very small portion of the population. Given that the standard deviation of the cereal-filling process is 15 grams, compute the standard error of the mean.

SOLUTION Using Equation (15.3) with $n = 25$ and $\sigma = 15$ the standard error of the mean is

$$\sigma_{\overline{X}} = \frac{\sigma}{\sqrt{n}} = \frac{15}{\sqrt{25}} = \frac{15}{5} = 3$$

The variation in the sample means for samples of $n = 25$ is much less than the variation in the individual boxes of cereal (i.e., $\sigma_{\overline{X}} = 3$, while $\sigma = 15$).

Sampling from Normally Distributed Populations

Now that the concept of a sampling distribution has been introduced and the standard error of the mean has been defined, what distribution will the sample mean, $\overline{X}$, follow? If you are sampling from a population that is normally distributed with mean μ and standard deviation σ, then regardless of the sample size, n, the sampling distribution of the mean is normally distributed, with mean $\mu_{\overline{X}} = \mu$ and standard error of the mean $\sigma_{\overline{X}} = \sigma/\sqrt{n}$.

In the simplest case, if you take samples of size $n = 1$, each possible sample mean is a single value from the population because

$$\overline{X} = \frac{\sum_{i=1}^{n} X_i}{n} = \frac{X_1}{1} = X_1$$

Therefore, if the population is normally distributed, with mean μ and standard deviation σ, the sampling distribution $\overline{X}$ for samples of $n = 1$ must also follow the normal distribution, with mean $\mu_{\overline{X}} = \mu$ and standard error of the mean $\sigma_{\overline{X}} = \sigma/\sqrt{1} = \sigma$. In addition, as the sample size increases, the sampling distribution of the mean still follows a normal distribution, with $\mu_{\overline{X}} = \mu$, but the standard error of the mean decreases so that a larger proportion of sample means are closer to the population mean. Figure 15.3 illustrates this reduction in variability. Note that 500 samples of size 1, 2, 4, 8, 16, and 32 were randomly selected from a normally distributed population. From the polygons in Figure 15.3, you can see that, although the sampling distribution of the mean is approximately[1] normal for each sample size, the sample means are distributed more tightly around the population mean as the sample size increases.

[1]Remember that "only" 500 samples out of an infinite number of samples have been selected, so that the sampling distributions shown are only approximations of the population distribution.

FIGURE 15.3
Sampling distributions of the mean from 500 samples of sizes $n = 1, 2, 4, 8, 16,$ and 32 selected from a normal population

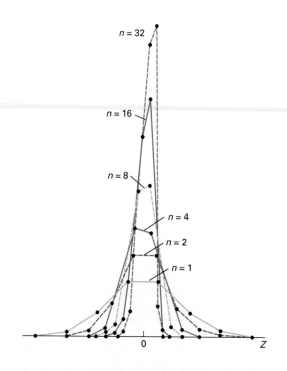

To further examine the concept of the sampling distribution of the mean, consider the Using Statistics scenario described on page 190. The packaging equipment that is filling 368-gram boxes of cereal is set so that the amount of cereal in a box is normally distributed, with a mean of 368 grams. From past experience, you know the population standard deviation for this filling process is 15 grams.

If you randomly select a sample of 25 boxes from the many thousands that are filled in a day and the mean weight is computed for this sample, what type of result could you expect? For example, do you think that the sample mean could be 368 grams? 200 grams? 365 grams?

The sample acts as a miniature representation of the population, so if the values in the population are normally distributed, the values in the sample should be approximately normally distributed. Thus, if the population mean is 368 grams, the sample mean has a good chance of being close to 368 grams.

How can you determine the probability that the sample of 25 boxes will have a mean below 365 grams? From the normal distribution, you know that you can find the area below any value X by converting to standardized Z values:

$$Z = \frac{X - \mu}{\sigma}$$

You studied how any single value, X, differs from the population mean. Now, in this example, you want to study how a sample mean, $\overline{X}$, differs from the population mean. Substituting $\overline{X}$ for X, $\mu_{\overline{X}}$ for μ, and $\sigma_{\overline{X}}$ for σ in the equation above results in Equation (15.4).

FINDING Z FOR THE SAMPLING DISTRIBUTION OF THE MEAN

The Z value is equal to the difference between the sample mean, $\overline{X}$, and the population mean, μ, divided by the standard error of the mean, $\sigma_{\overline{X}}$.

$$Z = \frac{\overline{X} - \mu_{\overline{X}}}{\sigma_{\overline{X}}} = \frac{\overline{X} - \mu}{\frac{\sigma}{\sqrt{n}}} \qquad (15.4)$$

To find the area below 365 grams, from Equation (15.4),

$$Z = \frac{\overline{X} - \mu_{\overline{X}}}{\sigma_{\overline{X}}} = \frac{365 - 368}{\frac{15}{\sqrt{25}}} = \frac{-3}{3} = -1.00$$

The area corresponding to $Z = -1.00$. Therefore, 15.87% of all the possible samples of 25 boxes have a sample mean below 365 grams.

The preceding statement is not the same as saying that a certain percentage of *individual* boxes will contain less than 365 grams of cereal. You compute that percentage as follows:

$$Z = \frac{X - \mu}{\sigma} = \frac{365 - 368}{15} = \frac{-3}{15} = -0.20$$

The area corresponding to $Z = -0.20$. Therefore, 42.07% of the *individual* boxes are expected to contain less than 365 grams. Comparing these results, you see that many more *individual boxes* than *sample means* are below 365 grams. This result is explained by the fact that each sample consists of 25 different values, some small and some large. The averaging process dilutes the importance of any individual value, particularly when the sample size is large. Therefore, the chance that the sample mean of 25 boxes is very different from the population mean is less than the chance that a *single* box is very different from the population mean.

Examples 15.2 and 15.3 show how these results are affected by using different sample sizes.

EXAMPLE 15.2

The Effect of Sample Size, *n*, on the Computation of $\sigma_{\overline{X}}$

How is the standard error of the mean affected by increasing the sample size from 25 to 100 boxes?

SOLUTION If $n = 100$ boxes, then using Equation (15.3) on page 193,

$$\sigma_{\overline{X}} = \frac{\sigma}{\sqrt{n}} = \frac{15}{\sqrt{100}} = \frac{15}{10} = 1.5$$

The fourfold increase in the sample size from 25 to 100 reduces the standard error of the mean by half—from 3 grams to 1.5 grams. This demonstrates that taking a larger sample results in less variability in the sample means from sample to sample.

EXAMPLE 15.3

The Effect of Sample Size, *n*, on the Clustering of Means in the Sampling Distribution

If you select a sample of 100 boxes, what is the probability that the sample mean is below 365 grams?

SOLUTION Using Equation (15.4) on page 195,

$$Z = \frac{\overline{X} - \mu_{\overline{X}}}{\sigma_{\overline{X}}} = \frac{365 - 368}{\dfrac{15}{\sqrt{100}}} = \frac{-3}{1.5} = -2.00$$

The area less than $Z = -2.00$ is 0.0228. Therefore, 2.28% of the samples of 100 boxes have means below 365 grams, as compared with 15.87% for samples of 25 boxes.

Sometimes you need to find the interval that contains a specific proportion of the sample means. To do so, you determine a distance below and above the population mean containing a specific area of the normal curve. From Equation (15.4) on page 195,

$$Z = \frac{\overline{X} - \mu}{\dfrac{\sigma}{\sqrt{n}}}$$

Solving for $\overline{X}$ results in Equation (15.5).

FINDING $\overline{X}$ FOR THE SAMPLING DISTRIBUTION OF THE MEAN

$$\overline{X} = \mu + Z\frac{\sigma}{\sqrt{n}} \tag{15.5}$$

Example 15.4 illustrates the use of Equation (15.5).

EXAMPLE 15.4

Determining the
Interval That
Includes a Fixed
Proportion of the
Sample Means

In the cereal-filling example, find an interval symmetrically distributed around the population mean that will include 95% of the sample means, based on samples of 25 boxes.

SOLUTION If 95% of the sample means are in the interval, then 5% are outside the interval. Divide the 5% into two equal parts of 2.5%. The value of Z corresponding to an area of 0.0250 in the lower tail of the normal curve is -1.96, and the value of Z corresponding to a cumulative area of 0.9750 (i.e., 0.0250 in the upper tail of the normal curve) is $+1.96$.

The lower value of $\overline{X}$ (called $\overline{X}_L$) and the upper value of $\overline{X}$ (called $\overline{X}_U$) are found by using Equation (15.5):

$$\overline{X}_L = 368 + (-1.96)\frac{15}{\sqrt{25}} = 368 - 5.88 = 362.12$$

$$\overline{X}_U = 368 + (1.96)\frac{15}{\sqrt{25}} = 368 + 5.88 = 373.88$$

Therefore, 95% of all sample means, based on samples of 25 boxes, are between 362.12 and 373.88 grams.

Sampling from Non-normally Distributed Populations— The Central Limit Theorem

So far in this section, only the sampling distribution of the mean for a normally distributed population has been considered. However, for many analyses, you will either be able to know that the population is not normally distributed or conclude that it would be unrealistic to assume that the population is normally distributed. An important theorem in statistics, the **Central Limit Theorem**, deals with these situations.

THE CENTRAL LIMIT THEOREM

As the sample size (the number of values in each sample) gets *large enough*, the sampling distribution of the mean is approximately normally distributed. This is true regardless of the shape of the distribution of the individual values in the population.

What sample size is *large enough*? As a general rule, statisticians have found that for many population distributions, when the sample size is at least 30, the sampling distribution of the mean is approximately normal. However, you can apply the Central Limit Theorem for even smaller sample sizes if the population distribution is approximately bell-shaped. In the case in which the distribution of a variable is extremely skewed or has more than one mode, you may need sample sizes larger than 30 to ensure normality in the sampling distribution of the mean.

Figure 15.4 illustrates that the Central Limit Theorem applies to all types of populations, regardless of their shape. In the figure, the effects of increasing sample size are shown for

- a normally distributed population in the left column.
- a uniformly distributed population, in which the values are evenly distributed between the smallest and largest values, in the center column.
- an exponentially distributed population, in which the values are heavily right-skewed, in the right column.

For each population, as the sample size increases, the variation in the sample means decreases, resulting in a narrowing of the width of the graph as the sample size increases from 2 to 30.

FIGURE 15.4

Sampling distribution of the mean for samples of $n = 2, 5,$ and 30, for three different populations

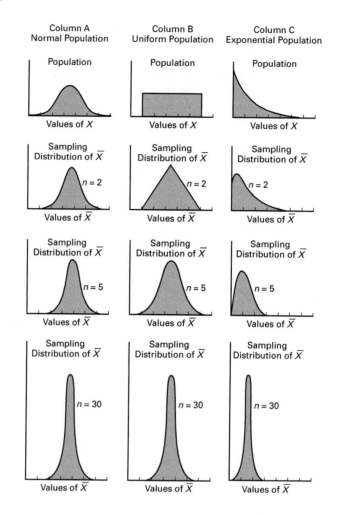

Because the sample mean is an unbiased estimator of the population mean, the mean of any sampling distribution in a column will be equal to the mean of the population that the column represents. Because the sampling distribution of the mean is always normally distributed for a normally distributed population, the Column A sampling distribution is always normally distributed.

For the other two populations, a *central limiting* effect causes the sample means to become more similar and the shape of the graphs to become more like a normal distribution. This effect happens initially more slowly for the heavily skewed exponential distribution than for the uniform distribution, but when the sample size is increased to 30, the sampling distributions of these two populations converge to the shape of the sampling distribution of the normal population. Using the results from all three distributions, you can reach the conclusions regarding the Central Limit Theorem that Exhibit 15.1 presents.

EXHIBIT   15.1

Normality and the Sampling Distribution of the Mean

For most distributions, regardless of shape of the population, the sampling distribution of the mean is approximately normally distributed if samples of at least size 30 are selected.
If the distribution of the population is fairly symmetrical, the sampling distribution of the mean is approximately normal for samples as small as size 5.
If the population is normally distributed, the sampling distribution of the mean is normally distributed, regardless of the sample size.

The Central Limit Theorem is of crucial importance in using statistical inference to reach conclusions about a population. It allows you to make inferences about the population mean without having to know the specific shape of the population distribution. Example 15.5 illustrates a sampling distribution for a skewed population.

EXAMPLE 15.5

Constructing a Sampling Distribution for a Skewed Population

Figure 15.5 shows the distribution of the time it takes to fill orders at a fast-food chain drive-through lane. Note that the probability distribution table is unlike Table 15.1 (page 191), which presents a population in which each value is equally likely to occur.

FIGURE 15.5
Probability distribution and histogram of the service time (in minutes) at a fast-food chain drive-through lane

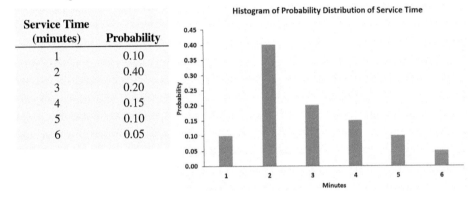

Service Time (minutes)	Probability
1	0.10
2	0.40
3	0.20
4	0.15
5	0.10
6	0.05

Histogram of Probability Distribution of Service Time

The population mean is computed as 2.9 minutes. The population standard deviation is computed as 1.34. Select 100 samples of $n = 2$, $n = 15$, and $n = 30$. What conclusions can you reach about the sampling distribution of the service time (in minutes) at the fast-food chain drive-through lane?

SOLUTION Table 15.3 represents the mean service time (in minutes) at the fast-food chain drive-through lane for 100 different random samples of $n = 2$. The mean of these 100 sample means is 2.825 minutes, and the standard error of the mean is 0.883.

TABLE 15.3
Mean Service Times (in minutes) at a Fast-Food Chain Drive-Through Lane for 100 Different Random Samples of $n = 2$

3.5	2.5	3	3.5	4	3	2.5	2	2	2.5
3	3	2.5	2.5	2	2.5	2.5	2	3.5	1.5
2	3	2.5	3	3	2	3.5	3.5	2.5	2
4.5	3.5	4	2	2	4	3.5	2.5	2.5	3.5
3.5	3.5	2	1.5	2.5	2	3.5	3.5	2.5	2.5
2.5	3	3	3.5	2	3.5	2	1.5	5.5	2.5
3.5	3	3	2	1.5	3	2.5	2.5	2.5	2.5
3.5	1.5	6	2	1.5	2.5	3.5	2	3.5	5
2.5	3.5	4.5	3.5	3.5	2	4	2	3	3
4.5	1.5	2.5	2	2.5	2.5	2	2	2	4

Table 15.4 represents the mean service time (in minutes) at the fast-food chain drive-through lane for 100 different random samples of $n = 15$. The mean of these 100 sample means is 2.9313 minutes, and the standard error of the mean is 0.3458.

Table 15.5 represents the mean service time (in minutes) at the fast-food chain drive-through lane for 100 different random samples of $n = 30$. The mean of these 100 sample means is 2.9527 minutes, and the standard error of the mean is 0.2701.

▶(*continued*)

TABLE 15.4
Mean Service Times (in minutes) at a Fast-Food Chain Drive-Through Lane for 100 Different Random Samples of $n = 15$

3.5333	2.8667	3.1333	3.6000	2.5333	2.8000	2.8667	3.1333	3.2667	3.3333
3.0000	3.3333	2.7333	2.6000	2.8667	3.0667	2.1333	2.5333	2.8000	3.1333
2.8000	2.7333	2.6000	3.1333	2.8667	3.4667	2.9333	2.8000	2.2000	3.0000
2.9333	2.6000	2.6000	3.1333	3.1333	3.1333	2.5333	3.0667	3.9333	2.8000
3.0000	2.7333	2.6000	2.4667	3.2000	2.4667	3.2000	2.9333	2.8667	3.4667
2.6667	3.0000	3.1333	3.1333	2.7333	2.7333	3.3333	3.4000	3.2000	3.0000
3.2000	3.0000	2.6000	2.9333	3.0667	2.8667	2.2667	2.5333	2.7333	2.2667
2.8000	2.8000	2.6000	3.1333	2.9333	3.0667	3.6667	2.6667	2.8667	2.6667
3.0000	3.4000	2.7333	3.6000	2.6000	2.7333	3.3333	2.6000	2.8667	2.8000
3.7333	2.9333	3.0667	2.6667	2.8667	2.2667	2.7333	2.8667	3.5333	3.2000

TABLE 15.5
Mean Service Times (in minutes) at a Fast-Food Chain Drive-Through Lane for 100 Different Random Samples of $n = 30$

3.0000	3.3667	3.0000	3.1333	2.8667	2.8333	3.2667	2.9000	2.7000	3.2000
3.2333	2.7667	3.2333	2.8000	3.4000	3.0333	2.8667	3.0000	3.1333	3.4000
2.3000	3.0000	3.0667	2.9667	3.0333	2.4000	2.8667	2.8000	2.5000	2.7000
2.7000	2.9000	2.8333	3.3000	3.1333	2.8667	2.6667	2.6000	3.2333	2.8667
2.7667	2.9333	2.5667	2.5333	3.0333	3.2333	3.0667	2.9667	2.4000	3.3000
2.8000	3.0667	3.2000	2.9667	2.9667	3.2333	3.3667	2.9000	3.0333	3.1333
3.3333	2.8667	2.8333	3.0667	3.3667	3.0667	3.0667	3.2000	3.1667	3.3667
3.0333	3.1667	2.4667	3.0000	2.6333	2.6667	2.9667	3.1333	2.8000	2.8333
2.9333	2.7000	3.0333	2.7333	2.6667	2.6333	3.1333	3.0667	2.5333	3.3333
3.1000	2.5667	2.9000	2.9333	2.9000	2.7000	2.7333	2.8000	2.6667	2.8333

Figure 15.6 Panels A through C show histograms of the mean service time (in minutes) at the fast-food chain drive-through lane for the three sets of 100 different random samples shown in Tables 15.3 through 15.5. Panel A, the histogram for the mean service time for 100 different random samples of $n = 2$, shows a skewed distribution, but a distribution that is not as skewed as the population distribution of service times shown in Figure 15.5.

FIGURE 15.6
Histograms of the mean service time (in minutes) at the fast-food chain drive-through lane of 100 different random samples of $n = 2$ (Panel A, left), 100 different random samples of $n = 15$ (Panel B, right), and 100 different random samples of $n = 30$ (Panel C, next page)

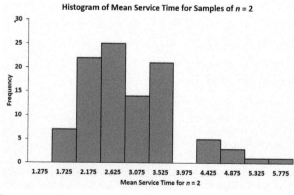

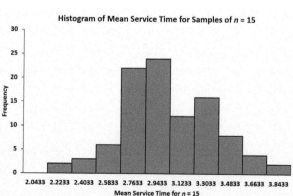

▶(continued)

FIGURE 15.6
(*continued*)

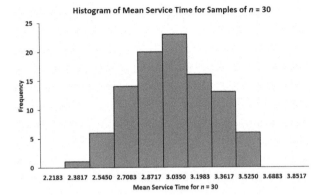

Histogram of Mean Service Time for Samples of *n* = 30

Panel B, the histogram for the mean service time for 100 different random samples of $n = 15$, shows a somewhat symmetrical distribution that contains a concentration of values in the center of the distribution. Panel C, the histogram for the mean service time for 100 different random samples of $n = 30$, shows a distribution that appears to be approximately bell-shaped with a concentration of values in the center of the distribution. The progression of the histograms from a skewed population toward a bell-shaped distribution as the sample size increases is consistent with the Central Limit Theorem.

VISUAL EXPLORATIONS

Exploring Sampling Distributions

Open the **VE-Sampling Distribution add-in workbook** to observe the effects of simulated rolls on the frequency distribution of the sum of two dice. When this workbook opens properly, it adds a Sampling Distribution menu to the Add-ins tab (Apple menu in Excel for Mac).

To observe the effects of simulated throws on the frequency distribution of the sum of the two dice, select **Sampling Distribution→Two Dice Simulation**. In the Sampling Distribution dialog box, enter the **Number of rolls per tally** and click **Tally**. Click **Finish** when done.

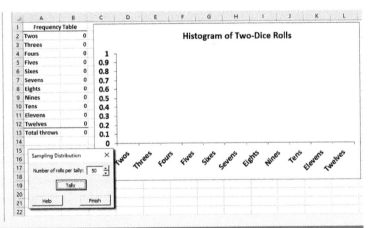

PROBLEMS FOR SECTION 15.2

LEARNING THE BASICS

15.1 A quality control officer heads a department that manufactures 1,000,000 units per annum. Answer the following:
a. Is it feasible for him to check all units produced or to check a sample of 1,000 units?
b. State the possible benefits the officer will avail by testing a sample rather than the entire population

15.2 Comment on the normality of the sampling distribution of mean when the
a. sample size is 5
b. sample size is 2
c. sample size is 30
d. sample size is 100
Do so for the following scenarios: population is normally distributed, fairly symmetrical and not normally distributed.

APPLYING THE CONCEPTS

15.3 Two researchers were given the task of analyzing the demographic characteristics of job fair participants. The first researcher collected a sample of 100, and the second researcher collected a sample of 500.
a. Which researcher is expected to get a higher standard deviation for the income of the participants?
b. Which researcher is expected to get a lower standard error of mean for the income of the participants?

15.4 The following data represent the number of days absent per year in a population of six employees of a small company:

   1 3 6 7 9 10

a. Assuming that you sample without replacement, select all possible samples of $n = 2$ and construct the sampling distribution of the mean. Compute the mean of all the sample means and also compute the population mean. Are they equal? What is this property called?
b. Repeat (a) for all possible samples of $n = 3$.
c. Compare the shape of the sampling distribution of the mean in (a) and (b). Which sampling distribution has less variability? Why?
d. Assuming that you sample with replacement, repeat (a) through (c) and compare the results. Which sampling distributions have the least variability—those in (a) or (b)? Why?

15.5 The amount of water in a two-liter bottle is approximately normally distributed with a mean of 2.05 liters with a standard deviation of 0.025 liter.
a. What is the probability that an individual bottle contains less than 2.03 liters?
b. If a sample of 4 bottles is selected, what is the probability that the sample mean amount contained is less than 2.03 liters?
c. If a sample of 25 bottles is selected, what is the probability that the sample mean amount contained is less than 2.03 liters?
d. Explain the difference in the results in (a) and (c).
e. Explain the difference in the results in (b) and (c).

15.6 The weight of an energy bar is approximately normally distributed with a mean of 42.05 grams with a standard deviation of 0.025 gram.
a. What is the probability that an individual energy bar contains less than 42.035 grams?
b. If a sample of 4 energy bars is selected, what is the probability that the sample mean weight is less than 42.035 grams?
c. If a sample of 25 energy bars is selected, what is the probability that the sample mean weight is less than 42.035 grams?
d. Explain the difference in the results in (a) and (c).
e. Explain the difference in the results in (b) and (c).

15.7 The diameter of a brand of tennis balls is approximately normally distributed, with a mean of 2.63 inches and a standard deviation of 0.03 inch. If you select a random sample of nine tennis balls,
a. what is the sampling distribution of the mean?
b. what is the probability that the sample mean is less than 2.61 inches?

c. what is the probability that the sample mean is between 2.62 and 2.64 inches?
d. The probability is 60% that the sample mean will be between what two values symmetrically distributed around the population mean?

15.8 The U.S. Census Bureau announced that the median sales price of new houses sold in 2016 was $316,500, and the mean sales price was $370,800.

Source: **www.census.gov/newhomesales**, April 1, 2017.

Assume that the standard deviation of the prices is $90,000.
a. If you select samples of $n = 4$, describe the shape of the sampling distribution of $\bar{X}$.
b. If you select samples of $n = 100$, describe the shape of the sampling distribution of $\bar{X}$.
c. If you select a random sample of $n = 100$, what is the probability that the sample mean will be less than $370,000?
d. If you select a random sample of $n = 100$, what is the probability that the sample mean will be between 350,000 and 365,000?

15.9 According to a report by App Annie, a business intelligence company that produces tools and reports for the apps and digital goods industry, smartphone owners are using an average of 30 apps per month.

Source: "Report: Smartphone owners are using 9 apps per day, 30 per month," 2017, **tcrn.ch/2qK4iRr**.

Assume that number of apps used per month by smartphone owners is normally distributed and that the standard deviation is 5. If you select a random sample of 25 smartphone owners,
a. what is the probability that the sample mean is between 29 and 31?
b. what is the probability that the sample mean is between 28 and 32?
c. If you select a random sample of 100 smartphone owners, what is the probability that the sample mean is between 29 and 31?
d. Explain the difference in the results of (a) and (c).

✓SELF TEST **15.10** According to the National Survey of Student Engagement, the average student spends about 15 hours each week preparing for classes; preparation for classes includes homework, reading and any other assignments.

Source: Data extracted from **bit.ly/2qSNwNo**.

Assume the standard deviation of time spent preparing for classes is 4 hours. If you select a random sample of 16 students,
a. what is the probability that the mean time spent preparing for classes is at least 14 hours per week?
b. there is an 85% chance that the sample mean is less than how many hours per week?
c. What assumption must you make in order to solve (a) and (b)?
d. If you select a random sample of 64 students, there is an 85% chance that the sample mean is less than how many hours per week?

15.3 Sampling Distribution of the Proportion

When analyzing a categorical variable, you often want to know what proportion of the data consists of one specific categorical value, or *characteristic of interest*. In the simplest case, a categorical variable that has only two categories such as yes and no, you calculate

studentTIP

Do not confuse this use of the Greek letter pi, π, to represent the population proportion with the mathematical constant that represents the ratio of the circumference to a diameter of a circle.

the sample proportion, p, that Equation (15.6) defines, as part of process to estimate the population proportion, π, the proportion of items in the entire population with the characteristic of interest.

SAMPLE PROPORTION

$$p = \frac{X}{n} = \frac{\text{Number of items having the characteristic of interest}}{\text{Sample size}} \qquad \textbf{(15.6)}$$

The sample proportion calculation is a simple fraction. For example, for a yes-no variable in a sample size of 5 responses, if there are 3 responses with the characteristic of interest yes, the sample proportion would be 0.6 (three fifths, or 3 divided by 5).

The sample proportion, p, will be between 0 and 1. If all items have the characteristic, p is equal to 1. If half the items have the characteristic, p is equal to 0.5. If none of the items have the characteristic, p is equal to 0.

In Section 15.2, you learned that the sample mean, $\overline{X}$, is an unbiased estimator of the population mean, μ. Similarly, the statistic p is an unbiased estimator of the population proportion, π. By analogy to the sampling distribution of the mean, whose standard error is $\sigma_{\overline{X}} = \dfrac{\sigma}{\sqrt{n}}$, the **standard error of the proportion**, σ_p, is given in Equation (15.7).

studentTIP

Remember that the sample proportion cannot be negative and also cannot be greater than 1.0.

STANDARD ERROR OF THE PROPORTION

$$\sigma_p = \sqrt{\frac{\pi(1 - \pi)}{n}} \qquad \textbf{(15.7)}$$

The **sampling distribution of the proportion** follows the binomial distribution, as discussed in Section 5.2, when sampling with replacement (or without replacement from extremely large populations). However, you can use the normal distribution to approximate the binomial distribution when $n\pi$ and $n(1 - \pi)$ are each at least 5. In most cases in which inferences are made about the population proportion, the sample size is substantial enough to meet the conditions for using the normal approximation (see reference 1).

Substituting p for $\overline{X}$, π for μ, and $\sqrt{\dfrac{\pi(1 - \pi)}{n}}$ for $\dfrac{\sigma}{\sqrt{n}}$ in Equation (15.4) on page 195 results in Equation (15.8).

FINDING Z FOR THE SAMPLING DISTRIBUTION OF THE PROPORTION

$$Z = \frac{p - \pi}{\sqrt{\dfrac{\pi(1 - \pi)}{n}}} \qquad \textbf{(15.8)}$$

To illustrate the sampling distribution of the proportion, a recent survey (L. Petrecca, "Always On: How You Can Disconnect From Work" *USA Today,* January 16, 2017, p. 5B) reported that 46% of American workers said that they work during nonbusiness hours. Suppose that you select a random sample of 200 American workers and you want to determine the probability that more than 50% of them stated that they worked during nonbusiness hours. Because $n\pi = 200(0.46) = 92 > 5$ and $n(1 - \pi) = 200(1 - 0.46) = 108 > 5$, the sample size is large enough to assume that the sampling distribution of the proportion is approximately normally distributed. Then, using the survey percentage of 46% as the population proportion, you can calculate the probability that more than 50% of American workers say that they work during nonbusiness hours using Equation (15.8):

$$Z = \frac{p - \pi}{\sqrt{\dfrac{\pi(1 - \pi)}{n}}}$$

$$= \frac{0.50 - 0.46}{\sqrt{\dfrac{(0.46)(0.54)}{200}}} = \frac{0.04}{\sqrt{\dfrac{0.2484}{200}}} = \frac{0.04}{0.0352}$$

$$= 1.14$$

The area under the normal curve greater than 1.14 is $1 - 0.8729 = 0.1271$. Therefore, if the population proportion is 0.46, the probability is 12.71% that more than 50% of the 200 American workers in the sample will say that they work during non-business hours.

PROBLEMS FOR SECTION 15.3

LEARNING THE BASICS

15.11 A testing company pre-tests a new drink. Of the 100 people who tasted the drink, 65 liked it.
a. Can you assume that the sampling distribution of the proportion is approximately normal?
b. Calculate 'p' for the sample proportion who liked the drink.

15.12 A random sample of 50 households was selected for a phone (landline and cellphone) survey. The key question asked was, "Do you or any member of your household own an Apple product (iPhone, iPod, iPad, or Mac computer)?" Of the 50 respondents, 20 said yes and 30 said no.
a. Determine the sample proportion, p, of households that own an Apple product.
b. If the population proportion is 0.45, determine the standard error of the proportion.

15.13 The following table represents the scores of students in Mathematics in the 10th grade. The dean of the school has announced a scholarship for students who score more than eighty percent.

| 75 | 40 | 55 | 43 | 67 | 87 | 64 | 98 | 69 | 56 |
| 45 | 93 | 41 | 89 | 65 | 79 | 76 | 90 | 70 | 71 |

a. Determine the sample proportion 'p' of the students who scored more than eighty per cent.
b. If the population proportion is 0.20, determine the standard error of the proportion.

APPLYING THE CONCEPTS

✓SELF TEST **15.14** A political pollster is conducting an analysis of sample results in order to make predictions on election night. Assuming a two-candidate election, if a specific candidate receives at least 55% of the vote in the sample, that candidate will be forecast as the winner of the election. If you select a random sample of 100 voters, what is the probability that a candidate will be forecast as the winner when
a. the population percentage of her vote is 50.1%?
b. the population percentage of her vote is 60%?
c. the population percentage of her vote is 49% (and she will actually lose the election)?
d. If the sample size is increased to 400, what are your answers to (a) through (c)? Discuss.

15.15 A tourism magazine surveyed 5,000 people for their expected travel plans in the following year. The response rate of the survey is seventy-five per cent. Forty-five per cent of the respondents of the survey agreed that they already have plans for their visits in the following year, while the remaining respondents said that they like to plan spontaneously. Assume that while preparing a research report for your hospitality class you conduct a similar survey and select a sample of 40 people.
a. Calculate the probability that the proportion that plans their visit in advance lies between 43% and 47%.
b. Calculate the probability that proportion that plans their visit in advance is less than 60%.
c. Determine the confidence interval that the proportion mean is 60% given the 90% level of confidence.
d. Determine the confidence interval that the proportion mean is 45% given the 90% level of confidence.

15.16 What do millennials around the world want in a job? A Deloitte survey of millennials on work-life challenges found that millennials are looking for stability in an uncertain world, with 65% of millennials preferring a permanent, full-time job rather than working freelance or as a consultant on a flexible or short-term basis.

Source: Data extracted from "Freelance flexibility with full-time stability," **bit.ly/2pr6h9r**.

Suppose you select a sample of 100 millennials.
a. What is the probability that in the sample fewer than 70% prefer a permanent, full-time job?
b. What is the probability that in the sample between 60% and 70% prefer a permanent, full-time job?
c. What is the probability that in the sample more than 70% prefer a permanent, full-time job?
d. If a sample of 400 is taken, how does this change your answers to (a) through (c)?

15.17 The goal of corporate sustainability is to manage the environmental, economic, and social effects of a corporation's operations so it is profitable over the long-term while acting in a responsible manner to society. An international study by Unilever reveals that 33% of consumers are choosing to buy from brands they believe are doing social or environmental good.

Source: Data extracted from "Report shows a third of consumers prefer sustainable brands," **bit.ly/2pTyEzO**.

Suppose you select a sample of 100 consumers.
a. What is the probability that in the sample fewer than 30% are choosing to buy from brands they believe are doing social or environmental good?
b. What is the probability that in the sample between 28% and 38% are choosing to buy from brands they believe are doing social or environmental good?
c. What is the probability that in the sample more than 38% are choosing to buy from brands they believe are doing social or environmental good?
d. If a sample of 400 is taken, how does this change your answers to (a) through (c)?

15.18 According to the MSCI 2016 Survey of Women on Boards, women hold 20% of director seats on U.S. corporate boards. This study also reports that 34% of U.S. companies have three or more female board directors.

Source: Data extracted from "The Tipping Point: Women on Boards and Financial Performance," **bit.ly/2pYDt9A**.

If you select a random sample of 200 U.S. companies,
a. what is the probability that the sample will have between 30% and 38% U.S. companies that have three or more female board directors?
b. the probability is 90% that the sample percentage of U.S. companies that have three or more female board directors will be contained within what symmetrical limits of the population percentage?
c. the probability is 95% that the sample percentage of U.S. companies that have three or more female board directors will be contained within what symmetrical limits of the population percentage?

15.19 The topic of global warming increasingly appears in the news. It has the potential to impact companies' operations through changes in governmental regulations, new reporting requirements, necessary operational changes, and so on. The Institute of Management Accountants (IMA) conducted a survey of senior finance professionals to gauge members' thoughts on global warming and its impact on their companies. The survey found that 65% of senior finance professionals believe that global warming is having a significant impact on the environment.

Source: Data extracted from "Global Warming: How Has It Affected Your Company?" **bit.ly/2pd341h**.

Suppose that you select a sample of 100 senior finance professionals.
a. What is the probability that the sample percentage indicating global warming is having a significant impact on the environment will be between 64% and 69%?
b. The probability is 90% that the sample percentage will be contained within what symmetrical limits of the population percentage?
c. The probability is 95% that the sample percentage will be contained within what symmetrical limits of the population percentage?
d. Suppose you selected a sample of 400 senior finance professionals. How does this change your answers in (a) through (c)?

15.20 An IAB study on the state of original digital video showed that original data video is becoming increasingly popular. Original digital video is defined as professionally produced video only for ad-supported online distribution and viewing (not TV). According to IAB data, 26% of American adults 18+ watch original digital videos each month.

Source: Data extracted from "IAB Original Digital Video Consumer Study," May 2016, **bit.ly/2aUPkzk**.

a. Suppose that you take a sample of 100 U.S. adults. If the population proportion of U.S. adults who watch original digital videos is 0.26, what is the probability that fewer than 21% in your sample will watch digital videos?
b. Suppose that you take a sample of 500 U.S. adults. If the population proportion of U.S. adults who watch original digital videos is 0.26, what is the probability that fewer than 21% in your sample will watch digital videos?
c. Discuss the effect of sample size on the sampling distribution of the proportion in general and the effect on the probabilities in (a) and (b).

15.4 Sampling from Finite Populations

The Central Limit Theorem and the standard errors of the mean and of the proportion are based on samples selected with replacement. However, in nearly all survey research, you sample *without* replacement from populations that are of a finite size, *N*. The **Section 15.4 online Topic** explains how you use a **finite population correction factor** to compute the standard error of the mean and the standard error of the proportion for such samples.

▼ **USING STATISTICS**
Sampling Oxford Cereals, Revisited

As the plant operations manager for Oxford Cereals, you were responsible for monitoring the amount of cereal placed in each box. To be consistent with package labeling, boxes should contain a mean of 368 grams of cereal. Because weighing each of the thousands of boxes produced each shift would be too time-consuming, costly, and inefficient, you selected a sample of boxes. Based on your analysis of this sample, you had to decide whether to maintain, alter, or shut down the process.

Using the concept of the sampling distribution of the mean, you were able to determine probabilities that such a sample mean could have been randomly selected from a population with a mean of 368 grams. Specifically, if a sample of size $n = 25$ is selected from a population with a mean of 368 and standard deviation of 15, you calculated the probability of selecting a sample with a mean of 365 grams or less to be 15.87%. If a larger sample size is selected, the sample mean should be closer to the population mean. This result was illustrated when you calculated the probability if the sample size were increased to $n = 100$. Using the larger sample size, you determined the probability of selecting a sample with a mean of 365 grams or less to be 2.28%.

▼ SUMMARY

You studied the sampling distribution of the sample mean and the sampling distribution of the sample proportion and their relationship to the Central Limit Theorem. You learned that the sample mean is an unbiased estimator of the population mean, and the sample proportion is an unbiased estimator of the population proportion. The techniques of confidence intervals and tests of hypotheses commonly used for statistical inference are discussed.

▼ REFERENCES

1. Cochran, W. G. *Sampling Techniques*, 3rd ed. New York: Wiley, 1977.

▼ KEY EQUATIONS

Population Mean

$$\mu = \frac{\sum_{i=1}^{N} X_i}{N} \qquad (15.1)$$

Population Standard Deviation

$$\sigma = \sqrt{\frac{\sum_{i=1}^{N}(X_i - \mu)^2}{N}} \qquad (15.2)$$

Standard Error of the Mean

$$\sigma_{\bar{X}} = \frac{\sigma}{\sqrt{n}} \qquad (15.3)$$

Finding Z for the Sampling Distribution of the Mean

$$Z = \frac{\bar{X} - \mu_{\bar{X}}}{\sigma_{\bar{X}}} = \frac{\bar{X} - \mu}{\frac{\sigma}{\sqrt{n}}} \qquad (15.4)$$

Finding $\bar{X}$ for the Sampling Distribution of the Mean

$$\bar{X} = \mu + Z\frac{\sigma}{\sqrt{n}} \qquad (15.5)$$

Sample Proportion

$$p = \frac{X}{n} \qquad (15.6)$$

Standard Error of the Proportion

$$\sigma_p = \sqrt{\frac{\pi(1 - \pi)}{n}} \qquad (15.7)$$

Finding Z for the Sampling Distribution of the Proportion

$$Z = \frac{p - \pi}{\sqrt{\frac{\pi(1 - \pi)}{n}}} \qquad (15.8)$$

▼ KEY TERMS

Central Limit Theorem
sampling distribution
sampling distribution of the mean

sampling distribution of the proportion
standard error of the mean
standard error of the proportion

unbiased

▼ CHECKING YOUR UNDERSTANDING

15.21 Explain the meaning of the terms 'statistic' and 'parameter'. Are they interrelated? How?

15.22 Comment on the variability of the mean of more observations from the population instead of one observation.

15.23 The duration of the meetings in a firm presents skewed distribution. Using Central Limit Theorem, comment on the distribution of the mean of a large sample of the meetings.

15.24 Why do you think investigating a sample is more efficient for statistical control than investigating an entire population?

15.25 What sample size is large enough to assume that the sampling distribution of the proportion is normally distributed?

▼ CHAPTER REVIEW PROBLEMS

15.26 According to a survey, the average number of 9 ounce coffee cups consumed daily is 3.1

(Source: **http://www.statisticbrain.com/coffee-drinking-statistics/**).

Assume that the standard deviation is 0.5 cup. A researcher surveys the daily coffee consumption habits in the state of Washington D.C. He draws a sample of 36. Calculate the probability that the sample mean will be

a. between 3 and 3.01?
b. greater than 3.2?
c. less than 3?
d. Calculate the range of the sample average mean for the midle95% area within which the sample means will lie.
e. If the researcher is willing to limit the standard error to 1.5% of population mean, is the sample size large enough?
f. If the researcher is willing to limit the standard error to 3% of population mean, then what should be the sample size?

15.27 The annual average return of S&P 500 from 1950-2002 was calculated as 9.7% with the standard deviation of 15.5%

(Source: **Hirshey, 2003**).

A person, who is going to retire in 40 years, wants to invest in stocks.

a. Assuming that the above annual returns have been impacted by extreme values, comment on the normality of the stock return over the next 49 years.
b. What is the probability that the mean return will be more than 15%?
c. What is the probability that the mean return is less that 5%?

15.28 An orange juice producer buys oranges from a large orange grove that has one variety of orange. The amount of juice squeezed from these oranges is approximately normally distributed, with a mean of 4.70 ounces and a standard deviation of 0.40 ounce. Suppose that you select a sample of 25 oranges.

a. What is the probability that the sample mean amount of juice will be at least 4.60 ounces?
b. The probability is 70% that the sample mean amount of juice will be contained between what two values symmetrically distributed around the population mean?
c. The probability is 77% that the sample mean amount of juice will be greater than what value?

15.29 In Problem 15.28, suppose that the mean amount of juice squeezed is 5.0 ounces.

a. What is the probability that the sample mean amount of juice will be at least 4.60 ounces?
b. The probability is 70% that the sample mean amount of juice will be contained between what two values symmetrically distributed around the population mean?
c. The probability is 77% that the sample mean amount of juice will be greater than what value?
d. Compare the results of (a) through (c) with the results of Problem 15.28 (a) through (c).

15.30 The stock market in Canada reported strong returns in 2016. The population of stocks earned a mean return of 17.5% in 2016.

Source: Data extracted from *The Wall Street Journal*, December 31, 2016–Janaury 1, 2017, p. B6.

Assume that the returns for stocks on the Canadian stock market were distributed as a normal variable, with a mean of 17.5 and a standard deviation of 20. If you selected a random sample of 16 stocks from this population, what is the probability that the sample would have a mean return

a. less than 0 (i.e., a loss)?
b. between 0 and 10?
c. greater than 10?

15.31 The article mentioned in Problem 15.30 reported that the stock market in Germany had a mean return of 6.9% in 2016. Assume that the returns for stocks on the German stock market were distributed normally, with a mean of 6.9 and a standard deviation of 10. If you select an individual stock from this population, what is the probability that it would have a return

a. less than 0 (i.e., a loss)?
b. between −10 and −20?
c. greater than −5?

If you selected a random sample of four stocks from this population, what is the probability that the sample would have a mean return

d. less than 0 (a loss)?
e. between −10 and −20?
f. greater than −5?
g. Compare your results in parts (d) through (f) to those in (a) through (c).

15.32 (Class Project) The table of random numbers is an example of a uniform distribution because each digit is equally likely to occur. Starting in the row corresponding to the day of the month in which you were born, use a table of random numbers to take one digit at a time.

Select five different samples each of $n = 2$, $n = 5$, and $n = 10$. Compute the sample mean of each sample. Develop a frequency distribution of the sample means for the results of the entire class, based on samples of sizes $n = 2$, $n = 5$, and $n = 10$.

What can be said about the shape of the sampling distribution for each of these sample sizes?

15.33 (Class Project) The webpage random.org allows you to flip various coins up to 200 times. Choose your country's coins and flip ten of them. Count the number of heads. Imagine you flip each of the 10 coins many times. What do you expect? Can you get 10 heads? Explain.

15.34 (Class Project) The number of cars waiting in line at a car wash is distributed as follows:

Number of Cars	Probability
0	0.25
1	0.40
2	0.20
3	0.10
4	0.04
5	0.01

You can use a table of random numbers to select samples from this distribution by assigning numbers as follows:

1. Start in the row corresponding to the day of the month in which you were born.
2. Select a two-digit random number.
3. If you select a random number from 00 to 24, record a length of 0; if from 25 to 64, record a length of 1; if from 65 to 84, record a length of 2; if from 85 to 94, record a length of 3; if from 95 to 98, record a length of 4; if 99, record a length of 5.

Select samples of $n = 2$, $n = 15$, and $n = 30$. Compute the mean for each sample. For example, if a sample of size 2 results in the random numbers 18 and 46, these would correspond to lengths 0 and 1, respectively, producing a sample mean of 0.5. If each student selects five different samples for each sample size, a frequency distribution of the sample means (for each sample size) can be developed from the results of the entire class. What conclusions can you reach concerning the sampling distribution of the mean as the sample size is increased?

15.35 (Class Project) The data in AnnualPrecipitation contains the average annual precipitation data in millimeters for 4,166 weather stations.

Source: Data extracted from
http://data.un.org/Data.aspx?d=CLINO&f=ElementCode%3A06.

a. Select 5 different samples of $n = 2$, $n = 5$, $n = 15$, and $n = 30$.
b. Compute the sample mean of each sample. Develop a frequency distribution of the sample means for the results of the entire class, based on samples of sizes $n = 2$, $n = 5$, and $n = 15$, and $n = 30$.
c. What can be said about the shape of the sampling distribution for each of these sample sizes?

CHAPTER

15

▼CASES

Managing Ashland MultiComm Services

Continuing the quality improvement effort first described in the Chapter 14 Managing Ashland MultiComm Services case, the target upload speed for AMS Internet service subscribers has been monitored. As before, upload speeds are measured on a standard scale in which the target value is 1.0. Data collected over the past year indicate that the upload speeds are approximately normally distributed, with a mean of 1.005 and a standard deviation of 0.10.

1. Each day, at 25 random times, the upload speed is measured. Assuming that the distribution has not changed from what

it was in the past year, what is the probability that the mean upload speed is
a. less than 1.0?
b. between 0.95 and 1.0?
c. between 1.0 and 1.05?
d. less than 0.95 or greater than 1.05?
e. Suppose that the mean upload speed of today's sample of 25 is 0.952. What conclusion can you reach about the mean upload speed today based on this result? Explain.

2. Compare the results of AMS Problem 1 (a) through (d) to those of AMS Problem 1 in Chapter 14 on page 184. What conclusions can you reach concerning the differences?

Digital Case

Apply your knowledge about sampling distributions in this Digital Case, which reconsiders the Oxford Cereals Using Statistics scenario.

The advocacy group Consumers Concerned About Cereal Cheaters (CCACC) suspects that cereal companies, including Oxford Cereals, are cheating consumers by packaging cereals at less than labeled weights. Recently, the group investigated the package weights of two popular Oxford brand cereals. Open **CCACC.pdf** to examine the group's claims and supporting data, and then answer the following questions:

1. Are the data collection procedures that the CCACC uses to form its conclusions flawed? What procedures could the group follow to make its analysis more rigorous?

2. Assume that the two samples of five cereal boxes (one sample for each of two cereal varieties) listed on the CCACC website were collected randomly by organization members. For each sample,

   a. calculate the sample mean.

   b. assuming that the standard deviation of the process is 15 grams and the population mean is 368 grams, calculate the percentage of all samples for each process that have a sample mean less than the value you calculated in (a).

   c. assuming that the standard deviation is 15 grams, calculate the percentage of individual boxes of cereal that have a weight less than the value you calculated in (a).

3. What, if any, conclusions can you form by using your calculations about the filling processes for the two different cereals?

4. A representative from Oxford Cereals has asked that the CCACC take down its page discussing shortages in Oxford Cereals boxes. Is this request reasonable? Why or why not?

5. Can the techniques discussed in this chapter be used to prove cheating in the manner alleged by the CCACC? Why or why not?

˅EXCEL GUIDE

15

EG15.2   SAMPLING DISTRIBUTION of the MEAN

Key Technique   Use an add-in procedure to create a simulated sampling distribution and use the **RAND()** function to create lists of random numbers.

Example   Create a simulated sampling distribution that consists of 100 samples of $n = 30$ from a uniformly distributed population.

PHStat   Use **Sampling Distributions Simulation**.

For the example, select **PHStat→Sampling→Sampling Distributions Simulation**. In the procedure's dialog box (shown below):

1. Enter **100** as the **Number of Samples**.
2. Enter **30** as the **Sample Size**.
3. Click **Uniform**.
4. Enter a **Title** and click **OK**.

The procedure inserts a new worksheet in which the sample means, overall mean, and standard error of the mean can be found starting in row 34.

Workbook   Use the **SDS worksheet** of the **SDS workbook** as a model.

For the example, in a new worksheet, first enter a title in cell A1. Then enter the formula **=RAND()** in cell **A2** and then copy the formula down 30 rows and across 100 columns (through

column **CV**). Then select this cell range (**A2:CV31**) and use **copy and paste values**.

Use the formulas that appear in rows 33 through 37 in the **SDS_FORMULAS worksheet** as models if you want to compute sample means, the overall mean, and the standard error of the mean.

Analysis ToolPak   Use **Random Number Generation**.

For the example, select **Data→Data Analysis**. In the Data Analysis dialog box, select **Random Number Generation** from the **Analysis Tools** list and then click **OK**.

In the procedure's dialog box (shown below):

1. Enter **100** as the **Number of Variables**.
2. Enter **30** as the **Number of Random Numbers**.
3. Select **Uniform** from the **Distribution** drop-down list.
4. Keep the **Parameters** values as is.
5. Click **New Worksheet Ply** and then click **OK**.

If, for other problems, you select **Discrete** in step 3, you must be open to a worksheet that contains a cell range of X and $P(X)$ values. Enter this cell range as the **Value and Probability Input Range** (not shown when **Uniform** has been selected) in the **Parameters** section of the dialog box.

Use the formulas that appear in rows 33 through 37 in the **SDS_FORMULAS worksheet** of the **SDS workbook** as models if you want to compute sample means, the overall mean, and the standard error of the mean.

▾**JMP** GUIDE

JG15.2   SAMPLING DISTRIBUTION of the MEAN

Use **New Columns**, **Tabulate**, and **Distribution**.

To create a simulated sampling distribution, use JMP random data generation features to create random samples of a sample size, then use Tabulate to create a table of sample means, and then use Distribution to construct a histogram and display tabular summaries about the set of sample means.

For example, to create 100 samples of $n = 30$ from a uniformly distributed population, open to a new data table and:

1. Click the **Columns red triangle** and select **New Columns** from its menu.

In the New Columns dialog box (partially shown below):

2. Enter **Column** as the **Column Name**.
3. Select **Random** from the **Initialize Data** pull-down list.
4. Enter **30** as the **Number of rows**.
5. Click **Random Uniform** and verify that the **Range** is from 0 to 1.
6. Enter **100** as the **Number of columns to add**.
7. Click **OK**.

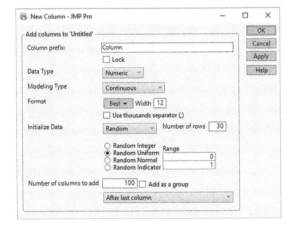

JMP inserts 100 columns of random data from an uniform distribution into the data table. With the data table still open:

8. Select **Analyze→Tabulate**.

In the Tabulate window:

9. Drag **Mean** from the statistics list and drop it in the **Drop zone for columns** area.

10. Click the **first column** in the columns list and then press **Ctrl+A** to select all 100 columns.
11. Drag the **selected 100 columns** from the columns list and drop it on the blank gray cell of the blank first column in the table. JMP displays a table of sample means in the Tabulate window.
12. Click the **Tabulate red triangle** and select **Make Into Data Table** from its menu.

JMP creates a new two-column data table of column names and means. With this new data table still open:

13. Select **Analyze→Distribution**.

In the Distribution dialog box (shown below):

14. Click **Mean** in the Select Columns list and then click **Y, Columns** to add Mean to the Y, Columns box.
15. Click **OK**.

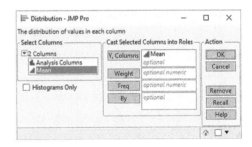

JMP displays a histogram and tables of summary information in the new Distribution window. Adjust contents of this window as necessary. Close the Tabulate window that remains on screen to declutter the screen.

Sampling from Normally Distributed Populations

Adapt the previous 15-step instructions to create samples from a normally distributed population.

For example, to create 100 samples of $n = 30$ from a normally distributed population, repeat steps 1 through 15 but in step 5, click **Random Normal** and enter the mean and standard deviation (in that order) in the **Mean/StdDev** boxes.

▼MINITAB GUIDE

MG15.2   SAMPLING DISTRIBUTION of the MEAN

Use **Uniform** to create a simulated sampling distribution from a uniformly distributed population. For example, to create 100 samples of $n = 30$ from a uniformly distributed population, open to a new worksheet. Select **Calc➔ Random Data➔Uniform**. In the Uniform Distribution dialog box (shown below):

1. Enter **100** in the **Number of rows of data to generate** box.
2. Enter **C1-C30** in the **Store in column(s)** box (to store the results in the first 30 columns).
3. Enter **0.0** in the **Lower endpoint** box.
4. Enter **1.0** in the **Upper endpoint** box.
5. Click **OK**.

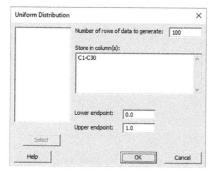

The 100 samples of $n = 30$ are entered *row-wise* in columns C1 through C30, an exception to the rule used in this book to enter data column-wise. (Row-wise data facilitates the computation of means.) While still opened to the worksheet with the 100 samples, enter **Sample Means** as the name of column **C31**. Select **Calc➔ Row Statistics**. In the Row Statistics dialog box (shown below):

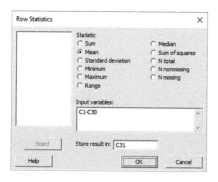

6. Click **Mean**.
7. Enter **C1-C30** in the **Input variables** box.
8. Enter **C31** in the **Store result in** box.
9. Click **OK**.
10. With the mean for each of the 100 row-wise samples in column C31, select **Stat➔Basic Statistics➔Display Descriptive Statistics**.
11. In the Display Descriptive Statistics dialog box, enter **C31** in the **Variables** box and click **Statistics**.
12. In the Display Descriptive Statistics: Statistics dialog box, select **Mean** and **Standard deviation** and then click **OK**.
13. Back in the Display Descriptive Statistics dialog box, click **OK**.

While still open to the worksheet created in steps 1 through 13, select **Graph➔Histogram** and in the Histograms dialog box, click **Simple** and then click **OK**. In the Histogram: Simple dialog box:

1. Enter **C31** in the **Graph variables** box.
2. Click **OK**.

Sampling from Normally Distributed Populations

Use **Normal** to create a simulated sampling distribution from a normally distributed population. For example, to create 100 samples of $n = 30$ from a normally distributed population, open to a new worksheet. Select **Calc➔ Random Data➔Normal**. In the Normal Distribution dialog box:

1. Enter **100** in the **Number of rows of data to generate** box.
2. Enter **C1-C30** in the **Store in column(s)** box (to store the results in the first 30 columns).
3. Enter a value for μ in the **Mean** box.
4. Enter a value for σ in the **Standard deviation** box.
5. Click **OK**.

The 100 samples of $n = 30$ are entered row-wise in columns C1 through C30. To compute statistics, select **Calc➔Row Statistics** and follow steps 6 through 13 from the set of instructions for a uniformly distributed population.